# A SKELETON
## IN THE
# DARKROOM
## STORIES OF
## SERENDIPITY
## IN SCIENCE

Gilbert Shapiro

*1817*

Harper & Row, Publishers, San Francisco

Cambridge, Hagerstown, New York, Philadelphia, Washington
London, Mexico City, Sao Paulo, Singapore, Sydney

*To Harriet, who made it happen*

Designed by Don Hatch
Illustrated by Alan Mazzetti

**Library of Congress Cataloging-in-Publication Data**

Shapiro, Gilbert
  A skeleton in the darkroom.

  Bibliography: p.
  Includes index.
  1. Serendipity in science. I. Title.
Q172.5.S47S53   1986      500      86-45024
ISBN 0-06-250778-8

FIRST EDITION
86  87  88  89  90  HC  10  9  8  7  6  5  4  3  2  1

# Contents

# Acknowledgments

My goal in writing these chapters was to make some exciting stories in science available to the general reader. I had no intention of competing with scholars who specialize in the history of science. Where it helped the narrative, actions and conversations have been reconstructed. Obviously, not even the scientists themselves are likely to remember the exact words years after they were uttered.

I have not tried to list the names of every person who was involved in these discoveries. The complete listing of Burton Richter's thirty-five collaborators, for example, would slow the narrative without really informing the reader. To those whose names have been omitted, I apologize.

I have relied heavily on secondary sources, which are listed in the Bibliography. Those whose interest in any of these adventures has been piqued are encouraged to learn more of the details by investigating some of the references.

I am grateful to the following people for useful comments, conversations, and correspondence: Luis and Walter Alvarez, Frank Asaro, S. Jocelyn Bell Burnell, William Chinowsky, Leo Falicov, Gerson Goldhaber, Troels Eggers Hansen, John Heilbron, Antony Hewish, Birgitte Hvidt, Max Knight, Helen Michel, Jim Peebles, Arno Penzias, Roy Schwitters, Harriet and Susan Shapiro, Henrik Smith, James Spohrer, Camille Wanat, and Robert W. Wilson.

Gilbert Shapiro
Berkeley, 1986

# Introduction

Serendipity is the art of finding something valuable when you are looking for something else. Everybody has had the experience. It happens when you find a lost wristwatch while rummaging through the dresser drawer for two socks that match. The surprise and delight at such good fortune can raise your spirits for days to come.

The word *serendipity* was invented by the English author and statesman Horace Walpole in a letter he wrote to his friend Horace Mann in 1754. Walpole had read a fairy tale, "The Three Princes of Serendip." (Serendip is the ancient name for Ceylon or Sri Lanka.) The princes in the story were "always making discoveries, by accident and sagacity, of things they were not in quest of." It was a familiar experience for which English had no adequate word. So Walpole coined the term *serendipity*, and it has remained a part of our language ever since.

Serendipity has played a crucial role in science. Some of the most important discoveries have been made by investigators who had no inkling of what they were about to find. Great breakthroughs in our understanding of nature, opening entire new fields of research, have come about because of unexpected, even accidental, findings in the laboratory.

Some discoveries can be made only serendipitously. If a whole new area of science is to be opened up, then by definition the field does not exist before the discovery is made. The scientist who makes it must therefore have been working in some other field. What the scientist was trying to do must have been something different from what he found. And this is the classic definition of serendipity.

It is like the case of the explorer charting small islands in the South Pacific, who suddenly comes upon the continent of Australia. The land was there all the time, of course, but other navigators had sailed completely around it without suspecting that the uncharted regions on their maps contained anything more than open ocean.

Serendipity is not synonymous with accident. It is not the same as pure luck. Both luck and accident play a role, but hard work, alertness, and perseverence are also demanded. Chance may throw a treasure in your path, but if you are not sharp-eyed enough to notice it, no one benefits. As Louis Pasteur once said, "Chance favors only the minds that are prepared."

The cliché of scientific discovery is familiar to moviegoers and readers of science fiction. A young, unknown, brilliant scientist happens upon a puzzling, seemingly trivial effect—a strange glow in the dark, a needle that jumps at an unexpected moment. Anyone else would dismiss the effect as an annoyance and work around it. But our genius senses a discovery of historic proportions in the making, a discovery that flies in the face of accepted wisdom on the subject. The young scientist pursues the puzzling phenomenon, wrings the cosmic significance out of it in a single cathartic moment, and presents it to a suddenly adoring world that, at the very least, awards a Nobel prize for the effort. The everyday lives of millions of people are changed forever because of this discovery.

None of these stories fit that cliché.

Few of these scientists were young or unknown when these events took place. Luis Alvarez was entering retirement and had already won a Nobel Prize when he formulated his dinosaur extinction hypothesis. Many of the others were in their forties and fifties, well established as professors at important universities. True, Arno Penzias and Robert Wilson were near thirty, and the ink was hardly dry on their doctoral theses when they found the microwave remnant of the cosmic Big Bang. But they are the exceptions. More often, experience was the key to recognizing the new and strange.

Wilhelm Roentgen's discovery of X rays is a classic example of serendipity. He went into his darkened room to try to make cathode rays (that is, electrons) emerge from his vacuum tubes into the air. The mysterious penetrating radiation that he found instead startled the world and led to a revolution in physics. He was fifty years old at the time.

*Genius* is not the best word to describe these scientists. We are not dealing here with Albert Einsteins and Isaac Newtons, but with more ordinary mortals. They possess above average intelligence, certainly, but probably have IQs no higher than the brightest student in your own class when you were at school. A more common characteristic is dedication to their work and the drive to keep going when nobody else is pushing them to achieve.

Most of these discoveries do not fly in the face of accepted wisdom; they bring new knowledge to the fore. The findings described in this book were so unprecedented that there was no wisdom about them, conventional or otherwise, until the experiments were done. The discoveries were so unexpected that nobody had even thought of them before. There was no previous thought with which to disagree.

After the fact, one can always go back and cite some theoretician who predicted something like the effect in question or some experimenter who had seen a similar effect and did not recognize it for what it was. These ante-cessors were so unsure of themselves that they didn't press their case more firmly. The earlier work was ignored or lost in the noise of innumerable reports—incorrect, incomplete, unimportant—that constantly fog the air of scientific enterprise.

A certain stigma may be attached to an "accidental" dis-covery. Scientists would rather have their work attributed to sagacity than to luck. Often they will insist after the fact that they knew what they were looking for, that the discovery had not been just a lucky accident.

Hans Christian Oersted's discovery of electromagnetism has been cited many times as a classic case of serendipity. At the end of a lecture demonstration in front of his class, so the legend goes, he passed an electric current through a wire lying close to a magnetic compass, and to his surprise he observed the needle move in a way that had never been seen before. Oersted himself insisted that he had always been sure that there was a connection between electricity and magnetism. Had he not suggested it in an article printed seven years before the discovery? Then why hadn't he done the crucial experiment seven years sooner? No one else picked up the clue, either. The inexplicable blindness of re-searchers to make the observation that in retrospect seems so obvious is a recurring theme. Time and again we shall see that discoveries lay waiting for years and even decades, but nobody took the crucial step to find them. Only the advent of serendipity in the laboratory of the lucky discov-erer revealed them to the world.

On the other hand, we have an example of scientists who insisted that their work was indeed a lucky accident. The experimenters at the Stanford linear accelerator are adamant that they found the J/Psi meson while figuratively stumbling about in the dark, and not because they had inside intelligence about a similar discovery by Samuel Ting's group from MIT. The claim of serendipity can work both ways.

We have many other examples of workers in science who were looking for something other than what they found. Alexander Fleming was examining color changes in bacteria when he came upon penicillin. Antony Hewish was measuring the twinkling of radio light from the stars when his student, Jocelyn Bell, saw the first indication of pulsars. Arno Penzias and Robert Wilson wanted to detect the radio signal from the outer regions of our galaxy and found instead the remnant of the cosmic Big Bang. What each of these investigators found was far different from, and immensely more interesting than, what they were looking for.

These are tales of adventure. They take place in a strange and constantly shifting locale: the frontiers of knowledge. Here are seven true stories of pioneers who struck gold, the gold of unexpected discoveries in science.

Some of these discoveries—X rays, penicillin, electromagnetism—have had worldwide impact. Others are so new that their application has not yet been found. Some are important only for the way they have changed how scientists see the world.

The excitement of a scientific discovery lies in the discovery itself. These tales have the same intrinsic interest as adventure stories or detective novels. There is the challenge of the unsolved mystery, the climactic moment of breakthrough, the delicious thrill of being the first human being to learn of some truth, some fact of nature, that was hidden from all previous generations, and which for the moment is unknown to all the rest of society. Balboa witnessing the Pacific Ocean or Cardénas peering over the rim of the Grand Canyon could hardly have been more excited.

Few of us can make scientific discoveries, just as we cannot all be explorers or private detectives. But we can all try to understand what it is like to be there, how it must feel to be present at the moment of great discovery.

One of the characteristics of all the stories in these chapters is that in every case the results were remarkably easy to reproduce. X rays were being used in hospitals and shoe stores within weeks of the appearance of Roentgen's paper. Oersted's experiments with currents and compass needles were repeated as soon as the news reached Paris. The J/Psi meson was confirmed in Italy within three days of its announcement in California. New pulsars, new iridium deposits, new evidence of the cosmic microwave background were reported by researchers worldwide almost immediately after the first papers were published. The germ-killing abilities of penicillin were evident to any biologist who obtained a sample of Fleming's mold culture. All of these stories fall in that category of results that make colleagues and rivals in the field slap their heads and wonder, "Why didn't I think of that first?"

The wonder is, in many cases, that these discoveries were not made even sooner. The equipment and the ideas necessary for the experiment had been in existence sometimes for as long as ten or twenty years beforehand. Like the explorer who sailed around Australia without spotting it, the rival scientists could be moved to exclaim, "How could we have been so blind?"

Sometimes it was a matter of simply repeating a common experiment in a slightly different way. Oersted ran his current wire north and south over the compass needle rather than east and west, as it had always been done before. Roentgen applied especially high voltage to his evacuated glass tubes and carefully covered the tube with black paper to mask the light inside. Penzias and Wilson tried to measure absolute intensities of radio waves from the stars rather than subtracting neighboring regions of the sky. Hewish and Bell, the Cambridge radio astronomers, used short time constants rather than averaging out the noise over longer intervals. The Stanford physicists changed the energy of their accelerator in tiny steps rather than in the usual broad survey.

A common thread in these stories is that of scientific caution. The scientists could not believe what they were seeing. Roentgen feared that people would say, as he put it, "Roentgen has probably gone crazy."

Penzias and Wilson struggled for months to get rid of their annoying noise background. Sam Ting hesitated to announce his new meson until it became clear that the Stanford people had seen the same thing. Hewish and Bell left the intermittent signal from the pulsars on the back burner for many weeks while they pursued other experiments, finally being forced to investigate when the signal refused to go away. The Alvarezes kept quiet about the Cretaceous-Tertiary boundary iridium until they could come up with a plausible explanation of how a large asteroid impact could cause so many extinctions.

Few of these authors had the luxury of being able to wait for a complete explanation of their new effect before publication. Some of them offered theoretical suggestions, but these have usually turned out not to be the final word. Conversely, Penzias and Wilson pointedly refused to endorse any specific theory about their results, even though a very good idea (the one now generally accepted) had been suggested to them.

The emergence of scientific explanations thrives upon open debate. Once a discovery has been announced, many explanations can be proposed and rejected before a consensus is reached. This is the province of the brilliant theoretical scientists with vivid imaginations and powerful mathematics. The formulation of a scientific theory is often the work of many minds. By contrast, the work of experimental discovery often belongs to the individual scientist or research group alone.

Most of the discoveries in this book have been recognized by the award of a Nobel prize. That prize has its limitations; it cannot be split more than three ways. Not all the individuals who were involved in the discoveries have been so honored. The Nobel committees conduct their deliberations in secret, giving us little insight into the painstaking process that decides who is or is not to be laureate. All of the participants have been honored in many ways, none of which—not even the ultimate honor of the Nobel prize—can probably ever compare to the excitement of the discovery itself.

This book is not an exhaustive catalog of scientific breakthroughs. There have been many others of equal impact and unexptectedness. Discoveries such as nuclear fission, superconductivity, or artifical radioactivity all had the easily reproduced, "why-didn't-I-think-of-it-myself-first" quality of the stories here. Our choice of material was often dictated by the availability of sources and documents. There is room for many sequels.

Will there be more such discoveries in the future? Obviously, the answer is yes. Some of these breakthroughs have been very recent; the age of discovery is not over. Without doubt there are many more strange and wonderful discoveries waiting to be made unexpectedly by coming generations of scientists.

May we all be blessed with serendipity.

# A SKELETON
## IN THE
# DARKROOM

Wilhelm Roentgen used his newly discovered x rays to photograph the skeleton of his wife's hand. He used playing cards to measure the range of penetration of the rays, but it turned out that the rays went completely through the whole deck.

# 1. A Skeleton in the Darkroom: *The Discovery of X Rays*

Setting:      November 8, 1895
University of Würzburg
Germany
Protagonist:  Wilhelm C. Roentgen, 50
Professor of Physics

*The discovery of X rays is a classic example of seren-dipity in science.*

*Professor Roentgen, in his darkened laboratory, strained his eyes to detect the cathode rays that other scientists had reported. To this end he provided himself with vacuum pumps, high-voltage induction coils, sealed glass tubes, fluorescent screens, and other apparatuses needed for this study.*

*A mysterious glow, in a place where it shouldn't be, alerted him to the penetrating radiation, which he named X rays. The rays passed easily through thick books and wooden boxes, but not lead or steel, through flesh but not bones. Roentgen became so caught up in his work that he could hardly eat or sleep. He was afraid to tell anyone what he saw for fear they would think he had gone crazy.*

*He learned that he could record the X rays on photographic plates. This relieved him somewhat; though his eyes may have deceived him, the film would not. He took photos of the contents of closed boxes. He thoroughly frightened his wife by showing her a picture of the skeleton of her hand.*

*After seven weeks of working with X rays, Roentgen was ready to announce his results. His paper was printed rapidly by a local scientific journal. He sent copies of it, along with X ray photographs, to all the scientific centers of Europe. Within days the newspapers got hold of it. X rays were the sensation of the world.*

*The applications of X rays were immediately obvious. Surgeons used them to help set broken bones and to locate foreign objects in the body like bullets and shell fragments. Shoe salesmen were quick to install X ray machines in their stores. Roentgen was hailed as a great benefactor of humanity.*

*The value of basic research motivated only by the scientist's curiosity about nature, was never more clearly illustrated. If some medical doctors had given Roentgen the task of finding a way to examine broken bones, how likely is it that he would have tried to do the job with vacuum pumps and high-voltage coils in a darkened laboratory?*

Darkness comes early to Würzburg in November. Sunset is at half past four, local time. Even the kaiser's decree that all clocks in Germany must keep the same time could win back no more than twenty extra minutes of daylight.

Professor Roentgen waited impatiently in his laboratory for night to fall. The work he was doing required absolute darkness in the room. The dim glow of the cathode rays could be overwhelmed by even the weak light of a candle, much less a stray beam of sunlight through a break in the curtain. Tonight if all went well he would see the cathode rays. If he were very lucky he might even bring them out of their sealed glass tube and play with them in his very hands!

It had been known for several years that if you pumped most of the air out of a sealed glass tube and then passed an electric discharge through its interior, the tube would glow dramatically in vivid colors and patterns. The Englishman Crookes, the Prussian Hittorf, and others had made careers of staring at the eerie flickerings emitted by gas discharge tubes.

Up until this year, Dr. Roentgen had not paid much attention to this branch of physics. He had recently been kept busy serving a term as Rektor, equivalent to president, of the university. His research before this had concerned itself with solids and liquids, tangible substances that one could see and feel. The shimmering realm on the inside of evacuated tubes, which could be watched but never touched, seemed as inaccessible as the distant stars.

All this was changed by a report from Philipp Lenard, a physics professor at Heidelberg who specialized in cathode rays, that he had succeeded in getting some of the rays out of the tube and into the air. A thin aluminum screen had been cemented to an opening in the glass, and the electrical plates inside the tube had been positioned so that the beam of negative charges (what we now call electrons) would strike the aluminum. When the voltage was cranked up high enough, the cathode rays would emerge from the apparatus and glow weakly in the air outside. They didn't get very far, perhaps only an inch or two from the window, before the glow disappeared. But it was a beginning.

This was the effect that Wilhelm Roentgen was trying to duplicate. If the cathode rays could be brought out into the open air, there was no limit to the experiments that could be done with them. They might be bounced off mirrors, focused, bent, or prodded in any number of ways not yet imagined. You wouldn't have to build a special apparatus for each new experiment. You wouldn't have to seal it in glass, search for and repair the leaks, and wait endlessly for the pumps to create an adequate vacuum. Now, at last, perhaps one could find out what the cathode rays really were.

It had taken many months to get all the equipment together. The glass blower had to be taught how to make tubes in the proper shape, with metal wires passing through the glass without causing any leaks. A strong pumping system was needed, and a high-voltage electric supply. Some of the required materials were not easy to get. Roentgen had to write to Lenard himself for a sample of thin aluminum foil for the windows of the new tubes. The very foil that nowadays is sold by the roll at any supermarket was, in Germany in 1895, a scarce commodity.

The day had begun in the usual way. There had been a lecture for the students in the morning. Dinner at noon was the big meal of the day, followed by a nap, or perhaps a game of cards. In the afternoon there were administrative matters to be handled.

Meanwhile, Roentgen's laboratory assistant had been busy pumping the air out of the discharge tube. The pump was worked by hand, and the procedure was quite tedious. A flask filled with liquid mercury was connected by a rubber hose to the rest of the glass tubing. First the flask had to be lifted to a stand that was higher than the rest of the apparatus. The flow of mercury through the tubes would then trap some of what little air remained inside. Then the assistant had to move the flask to a lower stand and turn a stopcock, allowing the trapped air to be removed. Then it was time to repeat the whole procedure.

Hour after hour the assistant sat in the laboratory, raising the heavy flask, turning the stopcock, lowering the flask, turning the stopcock back, watching the pressure of the remaining air drop slowly, slowly. The experiments that Roentgen had in mind required a vacuum pressure better than ten thousand times lower than that of normal air. It took several days of pumping to achieve such a vacuum.

The Lenard tube with the thin aluminum port was not to be used this time. It had developed a small leak, so that it could not be evacuated well enough. Instead, an all-glass tube would be used. However, its walls were thicker than those of the Lenard tube, and they might prevent the cathode rays from escaping. Roentgen hoped to get around this problem by using a higher voltage.

The high voltage was provided by a Ruhmkorff coil. This consisted of a pair of concentric cylinders, one fitting snugly inside the other, each one wound with thousands of turns of copper wire. The coil works by electromagnetic induction. A small alternating current in the smaller coil can induce a higher voltage alternating current in the outer coil. If the ratio of turns of wire in the two coils is set up properly, the voltage across the ends of the outer coil can be very high. All one needs is an alternating current (a.c.) in the small coil to start with. Direct current would have been better for his ultimate purpose, but the high voltage one can get from induction coils works only with a.c.

Power companies did not yet provide alternating current to buildings in Würzburg. You had to make your own. The Ruhmkorff coil had an interrupter circuit to do this. It worked something like a doorbell ringer. The battery-driven circuit includes an iron clapper that is held in place by a spring. But when full current is flowing, it energizes an electromagnet. This magnet pulls the clapper away from its place, and the circuit is broken. As soon as this happens, the magnet loses its strength, so the spring can pull the clapper back against its contact bar. This contact closes the circuit again, energizing the magnet once more, and the cycle repeats. The device produces an alternating current, with voltage as often positive as negative.

Roentgen's apparatus was crude by present standards. The motion around the clapper produced a lot of buzzing and sparking. The high voltage at the output of the Ruhmkorff coil was far from steady, coming out in bursts and spurts that reflected the vagaries of the bouncing clapper.

Nor did Roentgen have a precise way of measuring the voltage. He had to test the length of the spark produced by the coil. At great risk of subjecting himself to electric shocks, he would bring a screwdriver, or something similar, close to the terminal and draw a healthy spark zapping and crackling across the gap. Roentgen's coil could produce a spark several centimeters long. It was certainly several thousand volts in strength.

Roentgen used alternating current, yet it did not produce the most efficient kind of voltage for his purposes. Only the moments of positive high voltage were useful for attracting the cathode rays. They were known to have negative electric charge. Since in electricity the opposite charges attract, electrons are accelerated across the tube only when the electric contact on the far side has a positive charge. The periods of negative high voltage, in between the positive peaks of the cycle, were dead time in the process. Fortunately, the cathode ray electrons moved very fast and could travel completely across the tube during the positive swings of the voltage. What he expected to observe were multiple bursts of the rays, following so closely after each other that the eye would perceive them as continuous.

Roentgen knew that the cathode rays would make a faint glow in the air if and when they emerged from the discharge tube. But this glow was likely to be overwhelmed by the light from inside the tube. The beam there was much more intense and could cause light emission from the few air molecules remaining in the evacuated space. Especially bright would be the spot where the cathode rays struck the glass walls. Roentgen had fashioned a mask of black paper, carefully fit to the shape of the discharge tube, to prevent any light from escaping. The paper had to be thin, so as not to impede the cathode rays themselves, but it had to cover the apparatus completely.

Roentgen did not trust his own vision completely. He suffered from color blindness. Also he had been treated for another eye disease (diagnosed as "keratitis phlyctaenularis") in his youth. He expected to amplify the air glow by letting the cathode rays strike some fluorescent crystals he had obtained. To make sure he did not miss anything, he had made a little screen, a sheet of cardboard coated on one side with a paste containing finely ground barium platinocyanide, a salt known to glow in the dark when struck by radiation of various types. A spot would shine from this screen from the place where the beam of cathode rays intersected it. In this way he hoped to see the exact size and shape of the beam.

One more piece of equipment was needed. He wanted to measure precisely how far the cathode rays penetrated through air or other material. This measurement would help determine whether he was seeing the same sort of radiation that Lenard had detected, or whether there was more than one kind of cathode ray. Roentgen reasoned that it was not accurate enough simply to measure how far the rays penetrated the air. The glow, dim to begin with, could become fainter as the beam spread out, until he could no longer follow it. Perhaps, instead, he could watch the spot on his screen, without moving it, while he inserted sheets of paper or cardboard between the discharge tube and the screen.

For this purpose, if he was to be accurate, he needed a series of pieces of cardboard of exactly the same size and shape and especially thickness. Maybe it was this experimental need that explains why, among the apparatuses in his laboratory, where few visitors were permitted and no social recreation took place, Roentgen had provided himself with at least two decks of playing cards.

Now that it was getting dark, Professor Roentgen was ready for the important work of his day. The laboratory assistants had left. There would be no more coming and going into the room. This was a necessary condition for the work he was doing. Once his eyes were adapted to the darkness, they could not tolerate a sudden door opening and flash of gaslight. Too many minutes would be lost waiting for his pupils to dilate again.

The curtains were closed and the lights extinguished. The first test was to make sure that the black paper mask covering the discharge tube was indeed tight. He positioned himself directly in front of the stand and threw the switch to start the high voltage coil. In the dark he could hear the interrupter circuit sputter and crackle. Carefully he examined the tube from all angles for the telltale points of light, for the small pinholes that would permit the escape of the bright discharge glow that he knew was filling the interior of the tube.

Good. There were no light leaks. The carefully fashioned mask was doing its job well.

There was no sign of the cathode rays yet either. That would come later, when he increased the voltage, when his eyes were better accustomed to the dark, when he could use the fluorescent screen to amplify them. (By the way, where had he left the screen?)

Now to turn off the voltage and get ready for the next step. Dr. Roentgen always proceeded systematically in this way. Each evening he would begin by repeating many of the steps he had gone through before to make sure that everything was as it had been, to satisfy himself that nature was indeed repeatable. If anything was amiss with the apparatus, he could find the problem early and fix it before he had wasted too much time. His hand reached for the switch.

What was that?

At the far end of the table a dim green line of light was fluttering, its brightness rising and falling in sync with the noise from the Ruhmkorff coil.

Damn! The cover must have fallen off the coil.

Rather than turn on the lights right away, he decided to make what investigation he could in the darkness. The high voltage coil was off to the side, not in the direction from which the light was coming. He supposed that he was seeing it reflected in a mirror on the opposite wall. First he wanted to make sure that the light he saw was really correlated with the high voltage.

He opened the switch. The flickering line faded away.

He closed the switch. There it was again!

A few more repetitions of this cycle convinced him. The light was definitely associated with the high voltage. But it was puzzling nonetheless. It was in the wrong direction to be coming directly from the coil. Yet it seemed too close to be a reflection in the mirror. The color was wrong, too—pale green, in contrast to the yellow sparks usually to be seen around the coil. Was his color blindness deceiving Dr. Roentgen again?

There was nothing to do but strike a match. Maybe he could avoid turning on the lamp and completely spoiling his adaptation to the darkness. Leaving the high voltage switch closed so he could keep his eye on the mysterious light, he found the match box and ignited a flame.

The light was coming from the fluorescent screen, left lying face up on the far end of the bench.

This was indeed strange. Was he already producing enough cathode rays to make the screen glow? The voltage was not yet high enough. Besides, he knew from Lenard's experience that cathode rays could only with difficulty be coaxed more than an inch or two through room-pressure air. The screen he was observing lay more than a meter away from the discharge tube.

He moved carefully around the table toward the screen. The high voltage switch remained closed, and the interrupter circuit crackled along. Now he extinguished the match.

First to find out where the source of the fluorescence lay. He lifted the screen by its handle and turned it from a horizontal to a vertical position. The thin streak of light became a roundish cloud on the screen. He moved it back and forth in front of him. The spot got smaller and brighter as he brought it closer to the discharge tube. Continuing in this direction he found that it was smallest and brightest when he brought it to just that spot on the Hittorf tube where the cathode rays were supposed to be striking it on the inside.

Something was emerging from that position, getting

through the glass wall of the tube, through the black paper mask, and through several feet of air, to make the screen glow.

Now he moved the screen in the opposite direction, away from the discharge tube. The cloud grew larger and dimmer, but it did not fade completely even when Roentgen had moved the screen as far away from the tube as he could get. Whatever was causing the screen to glow, it could not be the short-ranged cathode rays.

To make sure that he knew which way the source of the light was traveling, Roentgen now turned the fluorescent screen around so that the cardboard backing faced toward the tube. The fluorescent side, now facing away from the discharge tube, glowed just as brightly as when it had been turned the other way. Roentgen laughed. If this radiation can pass through glass and through two meters of air, he surely didn't expect to stop it with a few millimeters of cardboard.

How much material would it take to stop it? He reached for his deck of playing cards. As he by now expected, a single card made no difference at all. He interposed the whole deck between the discharge tube and the screen. No great change, not even when he used both decks together.

He began rummaging in the dark for other thick objects to place in the beam. There were some wooden blocks on the lab table. Would they make any difference? It was hard to tell. The spot on the screen was flickering so much that he could not be sure whether the presence of the wood block was having any effect.

Behind him on the shelf he located some books. He felt for the thickest volume, a thousand-page manual full of mathematical tables. Even behind this massive obstacle, the spot on the screen shone visibly. Would nothing stop these rays?

Now he began systematically to repeat his earlier observations. Moving the screen back and forth, he was able to convince himself that there was no mistake. The "influence," as he now thought of it, was proceeding in straight lines from the spot inside the discharge tube where the cathode rays hit, directly across the room. It was going through, not around, the obstacles he was placing in its path. No amount of wood or paper (or black printer's ink) in the way seemed to diminish its intensity.

There was a knock on the door. Who is it? It was the servant girl. Professor Roentgen was late for supper. His family was waiting upstairs, where they had living quarters. The investigation was becoming so interesting that he didn't want to leave it. But perhaps it was time to do some hard thinking. Reluctantly he turned off the voltage, turned on the lights, and joined his wife and niece at the table.

He had little to say to them. His mind was racing through the implications of what he had just been doing. He bolted his food and excused himself as soon as possible.

The most obvious interpretation was that there was some invisible beam, like ultraviolet rays but far more penetrating, proceeding across the laboratory, making its presence felt only by the glow it made on the fluorescent screen. But other explanations had not yet been ruled out. For example the discharge tube might be acting like some kind of magnet, able to attract nails even on the far side of a thick wall. In such a manner the "influence" might be plucking at the atoms of the fluorescent screen, making them vibrate and emit their greenish light. Only if he were able to stop the beam somehow would he be able to rule out this alternative.

Or perhaps at the age of fifty, Professor Wilhelm C. Roentgen was finally losing his mind! Maybe the strong electric discharge in the room, or the buzz and clatter of the high voltage circuit, was having an effect on his brain, making him see spots of light on the screen when nothing was really there. This possibility might be eliminated by showing the effect to somebody else. Not yet, he thought. Better not risk exposing his possible madness to others.

He usually did not return to the laboratory after supper, but this could not wait. If he did not work tonight, the daylight would prevent him from resuming his work until the next evening. That was far too long to wait. After supper he hurried back to the laboratory. Before turning off the lights again, he provided himself with an array of materials to test for their ability to stop the rays. There were sheets of various metals, bottles of liquids, chemicals of all kinds, whatever came quickly to hand.

He found quickly that a thick sheet of almost any metal could stop the effect. A sheet of lead foil only one-sixteenth of an inch thick was enough to blot out the spot of light completely. He could see the sharp shadow cast by the edge of the sheet when he moved it only partway across the beam.

So they were rays, after all.

It was time to turn on the lights and record his observations in his notebook. He needed a way to refer to the new radiation. It resembled ultraviolet (UV for short) in being invisible to the eye but making fluorescent crystals glow. but it could penetrate so many materials that would have stopped UV. The next letter of the alphabet is W, but that is too much like U and V. This radiation was clearly something different. Why not call it X rays, until its true nature could be determined? X, the unknown quantity.

The days that followed were full of activity. There were so many things to be tried, so many questions to be asked of nature.

Was there something special about the construction of

the tube that enabled it to produce X rays? Apparently not. All the discharge tubes he tried worked equally well. Even the Lenard tube, with its aluminum window, its leaks finally repaired, could serve as a source of X rays.

Which materials were transparent to X rays, and which were opaque? Lightweight materials like water, rubber, and aluminum were no obstacles to X rays, except perhaps in massive thicknesses. Heavier substances like iron or stone, unless in very thin layers, cast observable shadows. The heaviest metals, such as gold or platinum or especially lead, could stop the X rays completely. Even paints and glasses containing lead were effective shields.

Could the X rays be deflected in their path? Roentgen could find no way to do so. He made wedge-shaped prisms of rubber, wood, and glass, hoping to observe some refraction. There was not a hint of any such effect.

He could not change the path of the X rays with a strong magnet. This showed that the X rays carried no electric charge. However, he could divert the cathode rays, still inside the evacuated tube, with the same magnet. Unlike the X rays, the cathode ray electrons did have charge.

When, by using the magnet, he moved the spot where the cathode rays were striking the wall of the tube, the X ray spot moved with it. This proved once again that the X rays were being produced at that point. It did not matter whether the tube wall was made of glass or aluminum.

So many discoveries were waiting to be made, so many things to be learned! Each day Professor Roentgen waited impatiently for nightfall. He no longer interrupted his evenings to have supper with his family. He could not afford the time.

Another problem kept troubling him. Was there no way to detect the X rays except by looking at the flickering light spot in the darkened room? Was it really there, or was he seeing some illusion? Was there some way to record the presence of X rays that did not depend on somebody's eyesight?

He thought of taking a photograph of the fluorescent spot. But the light was so dim that it would require a long exposure to make it register on the film. And the spot danced and flickered so much that the image would be ruined.

Then it occurred to him that the X rays might make an image directly on the photographic plate. After all, the ultraviolet rays that they so much resembled were known to be photographic. And so he proceeded to attempt to photograph the X rays.

A lens and a camera were hardly necessary. The X rays would pass easily through the camera diaphragm and be undeflected by the lens. All that was needed was to place the plate itself in the X-ray beam for a while and then develop it. It wasn't even necessary to unwrap the paper that protected the plate from daylight. The X rays would easily pass through that.

To Roentgen's delight, the experiment worked. The X rays did expose the plate, and the image of the X-ray spot was easily visible when it was developed. He could now be sure that X rays were not just an illusion.

Photography was an immense aid to his work. He could measure the darkness of the X-ray spots on various photographs taken under different conditions and thus obtain a numerical estimate of how the X rays behaved.

More importantly, he was no longer restricted to evening hours. With the photographic method available, he could turn on his X-ray beam in broad daylight and expose his plates to whatever configuration of beams and absorbers was

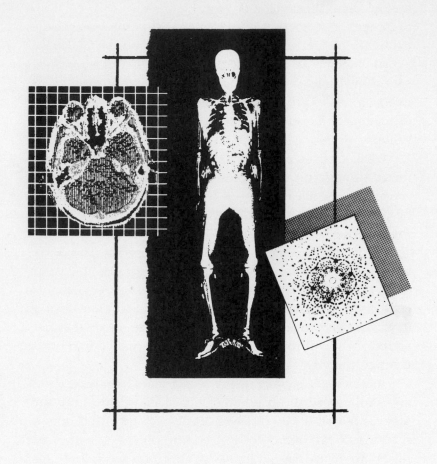

X rays can be used not only to photograph bones (*center*), but to re-
construct images of organs like the brain (*left*) and to learn the structure
of crystals (*right*).

of interest to him at the moment. Only the plate itself needed to be kept in the dark.

Of course one had to be careful not to expose the plates that were not being used yet. Roentgen kept all his spare plates in a different room and fetched them one at a time only when it was time to make the exposure. The high voltage and the X rays could now be left off most of the time. An experimental configuration could be arranged carefully, the plate put in place, and the switch thrown for the few minutes it took to make an exposure. Then the switch was opened again, and it was time to go to the photographic darkroom.

This method of operation probably saved Roentgen from the yet unknown effects of radiation exposure. Other workers with X rays suffered severe radiation burns and even fatal illnesses before it was realized that one must shield oneself from overlong exposure to the X-ray beam.

Roentgen himself built a shielded booth in his laboratory for quite a different purpose. He realized that it was easier to keep the booth dark than the entire room. A "window" of wood or black paper or thin foil served to let the X rays into the booth. This setup enabled him to work on his X rays in the daytime, at times when he did not want to have to wait for film to develop. Because the walls of the booth were lined with X-ray shielding material, and because the X rays were turned off when he came out of the booth, Dr. Roentgen avoided exposing himself unnecessarily to the rays.

Now that he could take photographs of the X rays, Roentgen realized that it would be interesting to use an X ray beam to form shadow images of ordinary-sized objects. The metal weights that he used with his chemical balance scale made ideal subjects. They were thick enough to be opaque to the X rays and small enough to fit in his beam. One of these weights, placed in front of a photographic plate, cast a sharp shadow that was easily seen when the picture was developed.

Ironically, the wooden box in which the weights were kept was transparent to the X rays. Roentgen was able to take an X ray photograph of the weights as they lay *inside* the closed wooden box. The box itself cast a bit of a shadow, especially at the spots where the wood was thickest. But the black shadows of the weights themselves stood out in dark relief.

This, then, was the miracle of X rays. The mysterious radiation enabled one to photograph the contents of a closed container from the outside. Even greater magic lay in store.

As he positioned objects in front of the fluorescent screen, Roentgen could not help but notice the faint shadow that his fingers cast as they moved in front of the X-ray spot. Down the middle of each finger image ran a darker line. What was that?

Closer inspection showed that the darker line had the shape of a bone. The joint was clearly visible at each knuckle. Roentgen was seeing the shadow of his own skeleton! The fleshy parts of his hand were nearly transparent to X rays, but the bones were not. The image he was seeing on the fluorescent screen showed clearly all the bones in his hand, as if the skin and tissues had been flayed away.

The specter must have alarmed Dr. Roentgen. Until that moment no doctor, nor anyone else in history, had ever been able to look directly at the bones of a healthy, living person. Skeletons were always associated with death.

But this was no death image. The ability to inspect bone structure without cutting into the living tissue would be an obvious benefit to the healing arts. Broken bones could now be diagnosed easily. The position of fractures could be pinpointed. The location of foreign bodies or abnormal bone growths could be spotted. A new medical technology would soon arise out of Roentgen's discovery.

No doctor, no scientist, not even Roentgen himself, could have anticiapted this breakthrough. Suppose some hospital, or some health ministry, had wanted Roentgen to invent a method to help them inspect broken bones. Would he have begun by building an apparatus of evacuated discharge tubes and high voltage coils? The value of basic research, directed only by the curiosity of the scientist about nature, was never illustrated by a more perfect example.

Roentgen now wanted to make a photographic record of this latest finding. He was distrustful as ever of the observations for which his own eyes were the only witness. But he could not X-ray his own hand. He had to be moving about the room during the exposure, throwing switches, setting up photographic plates, and making adjustments. A collaborator was needed.

But whom could he ask? Up to now he had shared his great secret with nobody. No one was even allowed into the laboratory except Roentgen and his assistants. The latter helped with carpentry, with pumping out the discharge tubes, and with some of the photography. But they were never present when the experiments were being done, and they had no idea what Professor Roentgen was doing. To the rest of the world, his family, his colleagues, there may have been some cryptic hints about his work, but no revelations.

He decided it was time to bring his wife, Bertha, into the laboratory. She at least was aware of his unusual activity, with his complete absorption in whatever it was he was doing. She could be relied upon to keep his confidence and not to proclaim to the world that her husband was a madman.

One evening in early December Roentgen brought his wife down to the laboratory. He directed her to place her hand over a photographic plate and hold it steady for several minutes. Then he went off to develop the photograph.

The skeleton of her whole hand was visible, not only the fingers but the tarsal bones inside her palm. Her gold wedding ring cast a dark shadow. The image of the fleshy outline of the hand could also be seen as a soft, faint envelope.

Bertha Roentgen was shocked. The idea of a skeleton was intimately connected with death. Her own health was fragile, and the possibility of a serious, threatening illness was always present. The ominous photograph could hardly have been reassuring. She retreated upstairs to the living quarters and participated no further in her husband's experiments.

Six weeks had now passed since that first night in the darkness with the flickering line on the screen. Christmas was approaching. The social obligations of the holiday season would leave him little time to continue his investigations. It was time to announce his results.

It was important to establish scientific priority. Other scientists could easily generate X rays. Once the method was revealed, any number of laboratories could reproduce his results within a few days. Therefore he had to make sure that his own report was in print before he made the results public.

He chose as his vehicle the Physico-Medical Society of Würzburg. This scientific society held regular meetings for members to present reports of their latest work, which were then printed in one of the society's publications. Roentgen had made no such oral report, but he asked the secretary of the society to put his paper in the next issue. Roentgen's position and reputation—he had after all been Rektor of the university—assured that his request would be promptly granted. The printing was accomplished within a few days. He could be sure that no scientific rivals would see the article before it was ready.

On the other hand, the proceedings of the Würzburg society were not likely to have a wide readership. So Roentgen supplemented its circulation by making use of the efficiency of the Imperial Postal Services. As soon as he had a few copies in his possession, he mailed them off to a selection of the leading physicists of Europe. Letters went off to Berlin, Vienna, Paris, and London. Some of the recipients were his personal colleagues; others were simply well-known scientists of worldwide reputation. In each envelope he enclosed a sampling of some of his X ray photographs: the box of weights, his shotgun, skeletons of the human hand or of a salamander. On New Year's Eve he deposited his announcements in the mailbox opposite the university.

After this, X ray developments were largely out of Roentgen's hands. One of the recipients of his mail showed the photographs to a newspaper reporter. Telegraph wires were soon jammed with the sensational news of the strange Roentgen rays. Here was a scientific discovery that the public could readily understand. The world became quickly aware of the existence of X rays.

Scientists and inventors were quick to jump on the bandwagon. Within weeks Roentgen's experiments were being repeated all over Europe and in America. Hospitals and individual doctors were already X-raying patients before the end of January. Even shoe salesmen were using X rays to show how well a shoe fit a customer's foot. In an age of fast communication, Roentgen's secret had become the world's knowledge almost overnight.

It took a while longer to answer the question that Roentgen had posed to himself: What was the true nature of the X rays? Today we understand that they are a form of electromagnetic radiation, like radio waves and visible light and ultraviolet rays. The principal difference is that X rays have wavelengths much shorter than the others mentioned, so short that these wavelengths could not even be measured until fifteen years after Roentgen's discovery. Each of the forms of electromagnetic waves has its own ways of interacting with materials, being absorbed by some, reflected by others, and finding certain materials to be quite transparent. Like the other forms, X rays can be produced by the deceleration of electrically charged objects, in this case by the rapid stopping of the fast electrons in the cathode ray tube when they slammed into the walls of the tube. At the time Roentgen could only guess that X rays were indeed another of the invisible forms of light.

While he had been careful to establish scientific credit for his discovery, Roentgen made no move to patent the X rays. He considered them the property of all humanity and did not wish to profit from their use. Not that he suffered financially. He had an established position in science, in the university, and in society. He received many honors and awards, not the least of which was the first Nobel prize in physics. But he declined to become a millionaire, preferring to let X rays become sooner and more easily accessible to everyone.

Roentgen was certainly not the first scientist to produce X rays. Lenard and other workers with cathode rays could not have avoided making X rays in the course of their experiments. They might even have noticed the fogging of photographic plates left unshielded in their laboratories. But none of them had the insight to recognize the properties of

X radiation. Roentgen's great contribution was to realize that something unusual was happening and to follow it up carefully to the point where he could be certain of the new results. Certainly some luck was involved in the discovery. But more than this, a lifetime of careful habits and the initiative to investigate nature in a region where few had been before had prepared Roentgen for this moment.

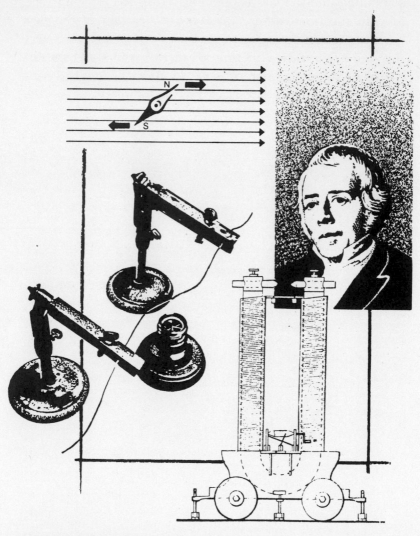

Hans Christian Oersted passed an electric current through a wire above a compass needle, and observed the needle deflect unexpectedly. This showed the connection between electricity and magnetism, and led to the invention of the electro-magnet (*lower right*).

# 2. Revelation in the Lecture Hall: *The Connection Between Electricity and Magnetism*

*Setting:*      April 1820
               University of Copenhagen
               Denmark

*Protagonist:* Hans Christian Oersted, 43
               Professor Ordinarius

*This is the one documented case of an important discovery in physics being made in the classroom, while the scientist was lecturing to his students.*

*Like many professors of his time, Hans Christian Oersted made ends meet by giving private lectures to which he charged admission. Oersted was a popular lecturer, in part because he illustrated his talks with demonstrations of the effects he was talking about. The audience in the winter of 1819–20 was advanced students of "natural philosophy," what we now call physics.*

*Oersted was later to write, "The preparations for the experiment were made, but some accident having hindered [me] from trying it before the lecture, [I] intended to defer it to another opportunity; yet during the lecture, the probability of its success appeared stronger, so [I] made the first experiment in the presence of the audience."**

*Oersted had long held the idea that all nature is uni-*

---

*Kirstine Meyer, ed., The Scientific Life and Works of H. C. Oersted. Copenhagen: A. F. Hoest & Son, 1920, p. LXIX.

*fied, that there is only a single set of laws that governs everything. Galvanism, what we now call the flow of electric current, seemed to show this neatly. The effects of galvanism were already known to include electric sparks, chemistry, light, and heat. Why shouldn't it extend to magnetism as well?*

*If, as he claimed, he had always known this should be so, he certainly had not been quick to carry out this simple experiment. Nor had any of the other scientists of the world. Even after the discovery in the classroom, work did not proceed. Oersted waited three months before repeating the experiment for reasons he himself later found difficult to explain. If not for that impulsive decision to try it in front of the students, how much longer would it have been before physicists realized the intimate relation between electricity and magnetism?*

*Oersted's discovery led directly to the invention of the electromagnet and its application to useful devices ranging from the doorbell to the telegraph. The theory of electromagnetism that developed from Oersted's finding was one of the great triumphs of nineteenth-century science.*

*Pay close attention to the next scientific lecture you hear. The lecturer may be on the brink of still another great discovery.*


It was time to light the candles. The students would soon be arriving for the lecture.

A brisk fire was burning in the hearth. It was needed; April in Copenhagen is still winter. The gathering clouds foreshadowed a thunderstorm.

The laboratory attendant stirred the coals, lit a fresh brand, and began going about his task. History does not record his name. We shall call him Frederik, since many Danish boys were named after their king.

Frederik was alone on the second floor now. The five medical students who worked there had departed from their laboratories earlier in the day. The professor was having tea in his family living quarters on the floor below. It would not be long before Hans Christian Oersted would be coming up the stairs to check the lecture preparations.

The title of the seminars was "Electricity, Galvanism, and Magnetism." Only the most advanced students could hope to follow it all. But Oersted, who was a poet as well as a physicist, had such a reputation as a clear and fascinating speaker that his talks had become very popular. Frederik had set out benches to hold over seventy people. Most of them would be occupied.

Oersted himself had been working on the apparatus that day. Some chemical flasks and trays had been set out. He wanted to demonstrate the influence of chemical effects on the magnetic state of iron. On the floor was a galvanic trough, the equivalent of what we today call an electric battery. The trough was an essential part of many of Oersted's experiments.

On the table was a magnetic compass, enclosed in a wooden case, and covered by a sheet of glass. In Denmark compass needles point slightly west of true north. The earth's magnetic north pole is in northern Canada, far enough from the geographic north pole to have a noticeable effect at this latitude. But this was only a small deviation, well understood and easily corrected. Oersted and his students knew very well which way was north. Today he would experiment with other ways of deviating the magnetic needle. Perhaps he could show a connection between galvanism (electric current) and magnetism.

As soon as he arrived on the second floor, Oersted began busying himself with connecting conducting wires to the two terminals of the galvanic trough. The cables were long enough to reach across the compass box on the table. "This time," the professor announced, "we shall run the wire north and south above the compass."

This was not the usual arrangement. If, as some scientists suspected, the current in the wire has some effect on magnetic elements, the most likely direction for the force that the wire exerts on the compass needle should be parallel to the wire. If the wire runs north and south, this argument says, the force will also run north and south. This makes the compass line up along the wire, the direction it is already pointing. Wouldn't it be more sensitive, went the usual reasoning, to run the wire east and west and watch the compass turn dramatically from its normal north-south to follow the east-west alignment of the wire when the current was turned on? That was the way the connection between electricity and magnetism had always been tested before.

None of those experiments had ever worked. If there was any connection between galvanism and magnetism, it had not been seen by running the current perpendicular to the compass needle. Now Oersted thought he knew why. He believed the force of the current in the wire ran not in the direction of the current, but at right angles to it. If his theory was true, then the way to test it was to run the wire parallel to the compass needle. That way, the needle might turn toward the east-west direction. It was worth a try.

Oersted had suddenly become so convinced that his new idea might work that he wanted to try it out right away. He hurried to make all the connections that would complete the circuit. A cable ran from the positive terminal of the galvanic trough to one side of the knife switch. From the other side a cable went to the vicinity of the compass box, where it was connected to a thin platinum wire. This wire ran across the glass plate of the compass; it was the active part of the whole circuit. The circuit was completed by the final cable running from the platinum wire to the negative terminal of the trough.

Oersted was about to do the experiment when the accident happened. The records do not tell us the exact nature of it, and we can only speculate. Perhaps the galvanic trough turned over, spilling acid on the floor, which would have to be cleaned up and replaced before the lecture. Perhaps one of the connecting cables snapped and a new one had to be made. At any rate, there was no time left to try the experiment before the students arrived.

Frederik stationed himself at the door to collect the admission price. Oersted was by this time a full professor and received a salary from the university. He no longer had to support himself by running a pharmacy on the side. He was able to rent living quarters for his family in the same building as the lecture room, on a street called Nørregade, where the university rented laboratory and lecture space. But the apparatus he used did not come free. In order to continue his scientific investigations, Oersted found it necessary to charge admission to his lectures from those students who could afford to pay it.

The lecture was going well, as usual. The students crowded around to watch the chemical demonstrations. Even the thunderstorm that struck while he was talking did not drown out Professor Oersted. On the contrary, he used the storm to help make one of his points. As each lightning stroke flashed through the windows, he called attention to the motions of the magnetic needle. It was evident that electric discharges had an effect on magnets.

Now was the time to try the galvanic circuit experiment. The effects of the accident had been repaired, and everything was ready to go. The platinum wire was stretched across the face of the compass, as exactly parallel to the direction of the needle as Oersted could make it. The experiment had not been tried before; one could not predict its result. In the course of the lecture, Oersted had so convinced himself of the likelihood of success that he was now willing to give it a try.

The knife switch was closed, and the current started to flow. The platinum wire became hot and began to glow. Oersted pointed out the effects of the galvanic current to his students. All eyes were fixed on the glowing wire.

Oersted and Frederik were watching the magnetic compass needle. It was no longer aligned parallel to the wire but was pointing northeast-southwest. Was this an illusion? The thunderstorm had by now ceased. Had it permanently affected the magnet needle?

Oersted ordered Frederik to open the knife switch. The glow faded from the platinum wire. The compass needle jumped about for a bit. When it settled down it was pointing in its original north-south direction, parallel to the wire. The previous change in orientation had been due to the current in the circuit and nothing else. Professor and laboratory attendant glanced at each other and exchanged a significant nod.

Well, enough of that, he continued in his lecture. There were other topics to discuss. If any of the students had noticed the peculiar behavior of the compass needle, they had made no comment. Their attention had been centered on the glowing platinum, not the compass. Oersted himself was so busy for the next three months that he did not find the time to repeat the experiment. But he continued to think about it and to devise improvements that would lead to a much more noticeable efect.

He still possessed the letter from his friend, Johann Wilhelm Ritter, predicting that this year, 1820, would see the next great discovery in electricity. Ritter had died penniless in Weimar long before his prophecy could be fulfilled. The idea behind it—that great electrical discoveries came every nineteen years, in step with the earth-moon rotational cycle—was, like many of Ritter's theories, a bit farfetched. But the prediction had after all come true. Remarkably, it had been carried out by the very person to whom Ritter had addressed the letter.

The last previous great discovery was, of course, the invention in 1800 of the galvanic cell by the Italian Alessandro Volta. With this tool one could produce a steady electric current in a circuit. A great new field of investigation had been opened, and the scientists of all nations had rapidly followed up on it. Among the most active investigators had been Hans Christian Oersted.

Looking back we can see that Oersted's experiment might have been done at almost anytime after Volta's work became known. But twenty years passed before the critical experiment was attempted.

True, these were years of constant warfare in Europe. Copenhagen was besieged twice by the British during the Napoleonic era. The kingdom of Denmark had undergone a national bankruptcy. But warfare in the early nineteenth century was not what it was later to become. Volta was able to communicate his results across the battle lines to the British Royal Society. The English physicists Humphrey Davy and Michael Faraday traveled across the channel to France while the two countries were formally at war. Clearly, the pursuit of science transcended national boundaries.

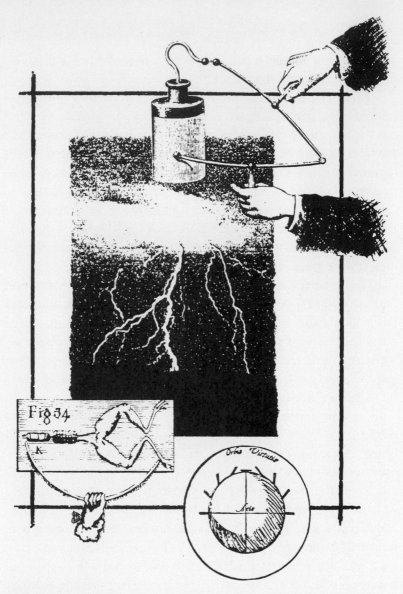

The sciences that were united by Oersted's discovery were electricity, represented by the Leyden jar (*top*) and lightning (*center*); magnetism, illustrated by Sir William Gilbert's model of the earth's magnetic field (*lower right*); and galvanism, or electric current, shown in Luigi Galvani's experiment with a frog's leg (*lower left*).

Oersted himself had made two long journeys through Germany and France during this period. In 1801, during a period of relative truce, he set out on a "wander-jahr," customary for young intellectuals at the beginning of their careers. In 1812–1813 he had taken a similar trip at a time when great battles were raging elsewhere in Europe. The personal contacts he had made with continental scientists helped to acquaint him with the latest developments and made Oersted well known to the leading scientists of Europe.

The subject that interested Oersted and his colleagues most was galvanism, what we today know as the electric current. Luigi Galvani, an Italian physician and a dabbler in sciences, had observed during the last decade of the eighteenth century that the leg of a dissected frog twitches in the presence of an electrical apparatus. Galvani thought the effect was coming from the muscle tissue, and he referred to it as "animal electricity."

Volta set the matter straight. It was the electrical discharge that triggered the muscles and caused various other effects unrelated to animal tissue. Nevertheless, Volta honored his countryman by calling the effect "galvanism." The name has stuck. We still measure current with galvanometers, and we plate metals by the process of galvanization.

Even at that early date, the connection between galvanism and electricity must have been clear. A galvanic circuit could be used to charge up a Leyden jar (what we now call a capacitor) even faster than the usual method of electrification by contact. Galvanism, or electric current, we now know, is simply the motion of electric charges through metal wires and other electrically conducting materials.

Volta's invention made use of the fact that some metals have a stronger attachment to their electrons than others.

In a typical "voltaic" cell, a strip of zinc and a strip of copper are placed in contact with the same bath of a solution like sulfuric acid. Some of the zinc atoms move into the solution, leaving negative charges behind. Some of the positive charges in the liquid are deposited on the copper. If the copper and zinc are both isolated, enough charge will build up on the two strips to stop the reaction. Positive charges on the copper repel further charges from reaching it; negative charge on the zinc attracts back some of the positive ions from the solution.

If the copper and zinc strips are connected together outside the chemical bath with a cable of conducting metal, the charges deposited on the strips can flow around and neutralize each other. The reactions in the cell then continue, and current flows in the external circuit until all the zinc dissolves, or until the solution saturates. As long as the circuit is complete and the cell does not wear out, the galvanic current will flow.

It was soon recognized that if you increased the size of the metal strips, you could get more current to flow. On the other hand, if you connect cells in series, with the copper strip of one cell attached to the zinc of the next, this would help break down the resistance of some materials that were not such good conductors. In London and in Paris, experimenters constructed huge "batteries," hundreds of voltaic cells connected together. A cable from one end of this array, when brought near the opposite terminal, could produce spectacular sparks in the air.

Oersted had no such apparatus. His single-cell galvanic trough had produced only a feeble effect on the magnetic needle, but it was certainly visible. With a few more such cells connected together, he could probably produce much larger deflections. This summer, when the students were gone and he had more time, he promised himself he would return to the experiment.

The connection between galvanism and magnetism was a fitting climax to his years of concentration on both subjects. Oersted shared with Ritter a belief in the unity of nature. There should be a single cause, they thought, behind all physical phenomena. Various scientists studied mechanics or chemistry or electricity. When the true nature of all these studies was understood, they argued, there should emerge a single law of nature that governed everything.

Galvanism seemed to be a link among many disciplines. The connection with static electricity had been obvious as early as the times of Galvani and Volta. The relation to chemistry could be seen in the construction of the voltaic cell. Moreover, when the two wires at the end of a galvanic circuit were thrust into a cup of salt water, bubbles appeared near each wire, which turned out to be the hydrogen and oxygen of which the water molecules are composed. The process of breaking up water molecules into the atoms that make them up, by passing electric current through the water, is called electrolysis.

When galvanic current is passed through a thin wire—like the platinum in Oersted's circuit—the wire turns warm and begins to glow. Thus heat and light are also connected to galvanism.

The one discipline that had not yet been related to the galvanic current was magnetism. Ritter had searched for magnetic effects of galvanism and had failed. Others had observed some hints of the connection. There were many reports of needles struck by lightning that became magnetized, and of compass needles similarly struck that were either demagnetized or had their polarity reversed. Two Italians, Gian Domenico de Romagnosi of Trent in 1802, and Benedetto Mojon of Genoa in 1804, reported magnetic effects of needles through which a current had been passed. Somehow these results had been ignored or not understood. Nobody had reported a result, like Oersted's, where the affected magnet was detached from any electric circuit.

It seems incredible that twenty years of intense scientific activity had failed to reveal the magnetic effects of the electric current. The general opinion of European scientists seems to have been that electricity and magnetism were separate and unrelated effects. Nobody until Oersted was willing to challenge this accepted wisdom.

We are reminded of the story of the emperor's new clothes, by the Danish storyteller Hans Christian Andersen, where nobody but one innocent child was willing to brave public opinion by pointing out the obvious truth. Ironically, Andersen was a good friend of Oersted. The two Hans Christians spent much time together at Oersted's house. Oersted was by then world famous, while Andersen was still a struggling young dramatist and writer.

In July of 1820, Oersted returned to the magnetic experiment. He had delayed three months in following up on it. Most likely he was worried about damaging the platinum wire, which would be expensive to replace. He continued to think that the magnetic effect was present only when the wire was also emitting heat and light. If that were true, it would not help to increase the galvanic current, because the wire might melt and end the experiment.

It now occurred to him that maybe heat and light had nothing to do with it. In that case he could use an ordinary brass wire much thicker than the platinum. This wire could handle a much stronger current and have a greater effect on the magnetic needle. The powerful twenty-cell galvanic battery that he and his colleague Esmarck had assembled could now be used to full effect.

The conducting wire was again stretched north-south across the face of the compass box, within an inch of the needle but not touching it. The switch was closed to complete the circuit, with current in the wire near the compass flowing from north to south. The compass needle swung around forty-five degrees to northeast-southwest. No doubt about it.

Now the connections were changed so that the current flowed south to north. The compass needle swung in the opposite direction from before, pointing northwest-southeast.

Lifting the wire an inch or two away from the compass reduced the angle of deflection, but the force was still unmistakably present. Moving the whole wire sideward, east or west, had a similar result.

Putting extra slabs of wood, metal, or glass between the wire and compass needle had no effect. Neither did water, stone, or other nonmagnetic materials. The magnetic force was being transmitted across space without regard to anything in between.

Now the compass was placed on a platform, with the wire running beneath the needle. The same large deflections were seen, but in the opposite direction from before. Current running north to south deflected the needle to the northwest-southeast position.

What if the wire were run east to west, the way Ritter had always tried? If the wire passed over the center of the needle, there was no deflection at all. But if the wire was closer to one end of the compass, the needle strained to deflect up and down.

The secret was out. The magnetic force around a galvanic wire is circular in form. The lines of force loop around the wire like bracelets on someone's arm. A magnetic needle near the wire is always deflected sideways with respect to the current, always in the same circular sense all the way around. If the current is reversed, the deflection is sidewards in the opposite circular sense.

Oersted hastened to call in some of his colleagues at the university, professors of medicine and natural history, to witness the experiment.

More tests followed. The conducting wire could be made of any metal: gold, silver, iron, brass, lead, tin, even mercury. But the compass needle had to be iron. Needles of brass, glass, or gum were not affected. Magnetism, and not some other effect, was clearly involved.

On July 21, 1820, Oersted published a short summary of his results. It was written in Latin, which all educated Europeans could read. This may have been the last important scientific result announced in that language. Translations into English, French, German, Italian, and Danish were published in journals in those countries before the year was out.

Copies of the paper were sent to all the scientific centers of Europe. In 1820 this meant by horse or by boat. The telegraph, an invention made possible by Oersted's discovery, did not exist. It took six weeks for the news to reach Paris, by way of Geneva.

There it created a sensation. André-Marie Ampère, mathematics professor at École Polytechnique, quickly repeated Oersted's experiment and then did some of his own. He showed that wires carrying current exerted forces on each other. He constructed a coil of wire which, when carrying a current, behaved exactly like a bar magnet, except that it could be turned off or reversed simply by stopping or reversing the current flow. The science of electromagnetism was beginning to flourish.

Oersted himself continued to contribute to the science. He published papers over the following years, as well as textbooks and encyclopedia articles. He made several triumphal tours of European countries, including England, receiving many honors, awards, and acclaim for his discovery. In Denmark he was active in science education, helping to establish standards that are still being followed.

His discoveries did not end with electromagnetism. In 1826 Hans Christian Oersted reported a method to prepare pure samples of the chemical aluminum, giving him a share in the discovery of that element. He should also be given some credit for "discovering" Denmark's other famous Hans Christian, the poet and writer Hans Christian Andersen. Oersted predicted, quite correctly as it has turned out, that Andersen would be remembered longer for his fairy-tales than for his dramas and novels. The gift of prophecy was in the man.

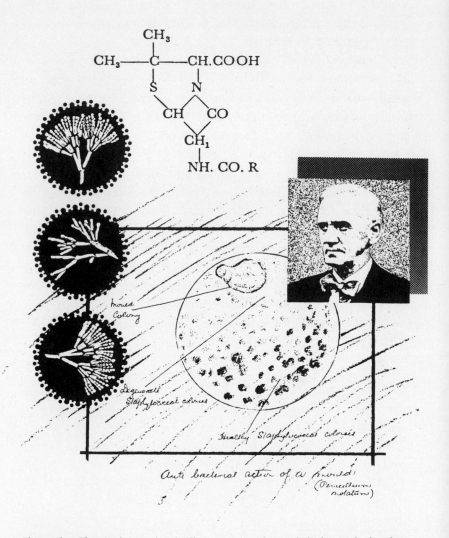

Alexander Fleming's notebook illustrates a culture dish (*center*) that became contaminated with *Penicillium,* a single-celled fungus (*microscope photos at left*) that somehow was killing the staphylococcus colonies in the dish. The bacteria-killing agent, penicillin (*chemical formula at top*) was the first successful antibiotic.

# 3. Painting with Germs: *The Discovery of Penicillin*

Setting:       September 1928
               Inoculation Department
               St. Mary's Hospital
               London
Protagonist:   Dr. Alexander Fleming, 47
               Bacteriologist

*The discovery of penicillin was a complete accident.*

*A culture plate, briefly exposed to the air, became infected with a fungus. Left untended on a laboratory bench through the summer vacation, the fungus managed to destroy the bacteria that were growing on the plate. It is an experiment that could not have been duplicated.*

*Dr. Alexander Fleming was about to throw the moldy culture plate away when he noticed what was happening. Reminded of another bacteria-killing agent he had once found in a similar way, Fleming moved quickly to preserve the fungus.*

*The mold,* Penicillium notatum, *that Fleming had found, produces a substance—which Fleming named penicillin— that is destructive to some of the most virulent bacteria that afflict humans. Not only that, but it is not toxic to animal tissues. Penicillin is the perfect antiseptic for diseases caused by these bacteria.*

*Fleming and his associates worked many months learning the properties of penicillin before he published his paper announcing its discovery. It worked nicely as an antiseptic in the test tube and culture plate, but not so well when it was tried on patients in the clinic. The researchers were not able to purify enough of the substance to make a full test of penicillin's usefulness as a medicine.*

*For the next twelve years, penicillin was used mainly as a laboratory reagent. It purified strains of bacteria that it did not affect by getting rid of all the other strains.*

*At the end of that period, a group at Oxford University's School of Pathology, led by Drs. Howard Florey and Ernst Chain, took up the study of penicillin. It was the initiative of the Oxford group, working under wartime pressure, that led to the development of penicillin as the wonder drug we all know.*

*Alex Fleming was an extremely lucky man. His first stroke of luck brought penicillin to his culture plate. And he found luck also in the work of the Oxford group that brought penicillin and its original discoverer to world acclaim. But Fleming was observant enough to notice the effects of penicillin and to preserve his unique mold culture—none like it has ever been found again growing wild in Europe—for posterity.*

Dr. Fleming was playing with microbes again.

One of his favorite games was to make what he called "germ paintings." He would sketch a scene within the confines of a four-inch glass Petri dish: a rock garden, a landscape, a dancing ballerina, or a flag. Then he would carefully fill each area to be colored with the appropriate culture medium and seed it with the right strain of bacteria. The whole dish was incubated at body temperature. By the next day the maturing colonies would appear, each in its own characteristic color: red, blue, yellow, white, pink, green, as

Alec Fleming had chosen. The whole scene would appear as if by magic on the floor of the dish.

Making these germ paintings was a difficult and painstaking task. It required the vision of an artist, the delicate hand and finger control of a jeweler or an optician, and the technical knowledge of a skilled bacteriologist. Alexander Fleming had all of these. He belonged to the Chelsea Arts Club, whose members must all be practicing artists. He had trained in the optical business run by two of his brothers. And he was a senior bacteriologist in the first clinical research laboratory in England, Sir Almroth Wright's Institute of Pathology at St. Mary's Hospital in London.

Beyond all this, Fleming took intense enjoyment in his work. It was the world's best game to play with his microscopic beasties, to learn their secrets, and make them do his bidding. Never mind that the one-celled creatures he was manipulating were the scourges of humanity, the causes of the worst diseases to afflict people and animals. If we are going to conquer these species, we must first understand them. Obtaining such understanding was both the business and the avocation of Fleming and the other doctors in the laboratory.

Once the germ paintings had developed, they could be fixed by spraying them with formalin vapor. This killed the bacteria and protected the culture from deterioration. The paintings could be displayed to visitors to the laboratory or shown on public occasions, such as the visit of royalty. They were shown to Queen Mary once at the opening of a new building. She was rather puzzled, and as she was leaving Fleming heard her say, "Yes—but what *good* is it?"

The answer to the queen's question was soon to be supplied.

Fleming was considered an expert on, among other

things, staphylococci, germs that cause boils and carbuncles and other surface infections. In 1927 he was invited to write a long article about these bacteria for one section of a nine-volume tome called *A System of Bacteriology* that was being published by the Medical Research Council. He had to read extensively in the medical and biological literature to prepare for this assignment.

A report about color changes in certain variants of staphylococcus aroused his interest. The species called *S. Aureus* produces golden yellow colonies when grown in the usual way. But, the paper suggested, if you cut the incubation short and left the culture at room temperature for a few days, interesting color changes took place.

Fleming decided he wanted to see these color changes for himself. They might be useful in the clinic for identifying the more virulent strains from each other. At the very least, he might be able to add some new pigments to his palette for germ paintings.

He had the help for a while of a research scholar named D. M. Pryce. But in February 1928, Dr. Pryce transferred to another department of the hospital, and Fleming had to carry on the color-change work alone. They were still good enough friends that Fleming could invite Pryce that summer to spend part of his vacation at Fleming's country home.

While Fleming was away from London, his laboratory room was used by Dr. Stuart R. Craddock, who had come to take Pryce's place. To make room for Craddock, some of Fleming's culture plates were piled in a corner, out of the sunlight and out of Craddock's way. There would be time enough to look at them when vacation was over.

In September, Fleming and Pryce returned to London, to their separate departments at St. Mary's. Fleming reclaimed his room and set about cleaning up his bench. The old cultures were inspected and, for the most part, discarded. There had been a heat spell in London while he was gone, and some of the staph colonies had begun to grow again. This would have subverted the color-change effect he was investigating, which was supposed to take place only at cool temperatures. There was nothing to do but submerge the cultures in lysol, an antiseptic that kills all the bacteria so the dishes can be washed safely, and start over.

Fleming had just placed a large pile of used culture dishes into the lysol tray when Pryce stopped by to see how the experiments were going. Fleming grumbled about having to do such menial tasks himself, now that Pryce had left. The summer experiment had not gone all that well, as Fleming was ready to show. He reached for one of the discarded cultures at random.

The dish he selected was at the top of the pile, well above the level of the lysol in the shallow tray. The culture inside it should still be alive. Too bad, because this particular dish had been contaminated by a fungus. The spores of these parasites were to be found in the air everywhere in such an old building on a busy street. No doubt one of them had landed on the plate while the cover was off. Now there was a large ugly blob of a strange mold growing at one edge of the dish.

There must be a better example to show Pryce, Fleming must have been thinking, as he prepared to place the moldy culture back in the lysol tank. But then something unusual about this plate stopped him. "That's funny," he muttered.

Half of the dish was covered with proliferating yellow colonies of staphylococcus, just as they filled most of the other dishes. At the edge of this growth, in a thin arc about one inch in radius centered on the mold, the staph cells were colorless and translucent. The edge cells looked as if they were dissolving away. Inside the one-inch circle there were no visible staph cells at all. To the trained bacteriologist, there could be only one conclusion. Something near the mold growth was destroying the bacteria.

It was a very lucky accident that brought that particular mold spore to that particular culture dish. But Alexander Fleming was excellently prepared, by training and by experience, to take advantage of it.

Once before in his life, Fleming had seen such a thing. It had led to the major work of his career up until then. In 1922 he had discovered an agent in the nasal mucus that can kill certain kinds of bacteria, just as this mold was doing six years later. He had named it "lysozyme." Lysozyme is found abundantly in tear drops, in egg whites, and in many other human and animal tissues; it forms one of the body's natural defenses against infection. Unfortunately for medical applications, the bacteria affected by lysozyme are all harmless species. Possibly it is their very susceptibility to lysozyme that makes them harmless. After a very promising start, lysozyme had turned into an interesting research topic, but a disappointment in the clinic.

The substance around the mold in 1928 was something different. It was, after all, attacking staphylococcus, which, Fleming knew, is unaffected by lysozyme. While staph is not usually a dangerous killer, it can cause severe pain to some patients, which this new substance might be able to cure.

Fleming moved to preserve the mold. Fortunately, the contaminated dish had not yet been submerged in the lysol. The fungus was still alive. He scraped a sample from the dish with a platinum loop—a standard tool of microbiologists—and placed it in a test tube with a liquid used for growing fungi. Over the next fifteen years, many generations of Fleming's mold would be grown in his laboratory and in other places where he sent samples.

Fleming also saved the original culture dish. A photograph was taken, to be used in publication. Once he was certain that the fungus subculture was thriving, he sprayed the original dish with formalin vapor, just like one of his germ paintings. He preserved it for many years, eventually donating the dish to the British Museum.

The next few days, Fleming showed his culture dish to anyone who would listen, insisting that something really interesting had happened there. Obviously he was excited by his discovery.

The excitement did not extend to his colleagues in the laboratory. Perhaps his dour personality was less than forceful. Perhaps they felt he had "cried 'wolf'" too often with lysozyme. Perhaps they each had their own concerns and their own lines of research that seemed equally promising. Fleming's discovery did not make a lasting impression on the research workers closest to him at the time.

The background behind the work then going on at St. Mary's Hospital may help explain this lack of enthusiasm.

By Fleming's time, the germ theory of disease was well established. It had been fifty years since the pioneering work of Louis Pasteur and Robert Koch. Medical science now understood that infectious sicknesses were caused by the action of microbic agents, one-celled creatures such as bacteria, fungi, and protozoa, or even smaller living objects known as viruses.

But knowing what causes a disease is not the same thing as knowing how to cure it. The list of ailments that could be treated effectively in 1928 was pitiably short. For most illnesses, a doctor could try to relieve the symptoms, encourage the patient, and hope that the body's natural defenses could overcome the disease.

Most chemicals that can kill microbes on a culture plate are deadly poisons. However, there are some compounds that can kill germs without being poisonous to humans. These are known as antiseptics. Dr. Joseph Lister, a Scot like Dr. Fleming, had promoted the use of antiseptics to destroy bacteria in the air of a surgical operating room. But most antiseptics are not the sort of thing a patient can swallow, much less have injected into the bloodstream. The search for a safe antiseptic was in 1928 an unfulfilled quest.

The group at St. Mary's had good reason to distrust antiseptics. Their experience in field hospitals during World War I, when antiseptics were administered freely to open wounds, had shown them that such application was worse than useless. The antiseptics being used killed the white blood cells, which protect the body against germs, more efficiently than they killed the germs themselves.

Chemotherapy, the use of artificially produced drugs to fight specific diseases, had enjoyed only one success before 1928. In 1910 Dr. Paul Ehrlich had created Salvarsan, a dangerous arsenic-containing compound that could cure syphilis. Dr. Fleming himself had made a sideline of treating syphilis patients with this drug soon after it was introduced.

Some microbiologists looked to chemicals produced by living cells. Many organisms, in natural competition with each other, wage a sort of chemical warfare, some of whose products might turn out to be useful in medicine. The word *antibiosis*, to describe this action, had been coined as early as 1889. There were many reports of searches for such substances before Fleming's work, but nothing useful had yet been found.

Vaccination was another approach. The introduction of

weakened disease carriers into the body can stimulate the body's immune system so that it can resist an attack of the disease itself. Vaccination has eliminated smallpox. Jenner used it against this dread disease even before the mechanism was understood. Pasteur showed how cattle could be protected from anthrax by this method. He dramatically saved the life of a rabies victim by injecting the vaccine after the disease germs were already present in the patient's body. Almroth Wright, Fleming's chief, had used killed germs to immunize patients against typhoid fever.

The clinical research laboratory that Wright organized at St. Mary's Hospital was committed to the principle that diseases could be cured by vaccinating the patient after he or she had already begun showing symptoms of the disease. It is an approach that, in retrospect, has not been greatly successful. But it was accepted by many doctors at the time, who, in truth, did not have many alternative treatments available. The laboratory supported itself by selling its vaccines to private doctors for treatment of their patients. The research equipment, the rental of laboratory space, and the salaries of the lab staff depended on this support. One of Dr. Fleming's major responsibilities was to supervise the manufacture of these vaccines.

Dr. Wright and the others would hardly be enthusiastic about a discovery that would make vaccine therapy obsolete.

Despite the lack of encouragement, Fleming resolved to follow up on his strange mold.

One order of business was to identify it. There was an expert on fungi, Dr. C. J. LaTouche, who had his laboratory on the floor below Fleming's. Fleming asked LaTouche what the mold was. LaTouche told him it was a species of *Penicillium*, green molds that grow on stale bread, ripening cheese, and decaying fruit. The mycologist who named the genus thought that the tuftlike ends of its branches resembled paint brushes; the same Latin root gives us the word *pencil*.

The bacteria in Fleming's culture plates were dying at some distance from the mold itself. Clearly, the *Penicillium* was producing some substance, some chemical, that could migrate away from its source and attack the bacteria where it found them. The exact nature of this chemical would require some investigation. But Fleming now had a name for it.

He would call the newly discovered bacteria-killing agent "penicillin."

The mold that Fleming preserved seemed to be identical with one of the species that LaTouche was keeping in his room downstairs. It is likely that one of its spores had found its way into the air, up the stairwell, in through the always open door of Fleming's laboratory, and onto the historical culture dish. LaTouche thought that it belonged to the species *Penicillium rubrum*, and Fleming accepted this identification. His shaky grasp of Latin told him that "rubrum" meant red. This fungus, on the other hand, became bright yellow as it matured. But he was in no position to question an expert. Anyway, an error in the name of the species would have no effect on Fleming's work.

As it turned out, LaTouche was wrong. Two years later, the American mycologist, Charles Thom, was sent a sample of Fleming's mold, which he correctly recognized as *Penicillium notatum*. Even within species, strains can vary, and Fleming's was certainly an unusual variant. Thom's own specimens of *P. notatum* did not have any of the germ-killing power that Fleming's samples had.

Neither did anything else. None of the other molds in

LaTouche's laboratory, nor any that Fleming could come up with independently, could kill bacteria. Penicillin was not like lysozyme, which could be found in so many tissues.

In the years since then, intensive searches by many workers have not yielded any species anywhere in the Old World that produces penicillin. (In 1943, a strain of *Penicillium crysogenum* was found in Illinois that is even more potent than Fleming's, and this strain is now used in the commercial manufacture of penicillin.) Fleming's strain of *P. notatum* has never again been found outside the laboratory.

In this as in many other aspects of his life, Alexander Fleming was an extremely lucky man. At a crucial moment in his early career, when he had been about to settle for a life as a clerk in a shipping firm, he had inherited enough money from his bachelor uncle to enroll in medical school. Later, in April 1914, he had resigned from the London Scottish regiment of reserves, in which he had served for fourteen years, just months before the regiment was to be decimated in the opening battles of World War I. In World War II, during the London blitz, he and his family twice escaped injury when their home was hit by German bombs. And in the late summer of 1928, a spore of just the right strain of *Penicillium* had landed on his culture dish at just the right moment to kill the bacteria and to be noticed by Fleming before the whole culture was lost in the lysol tank.

Fleming began investigating what other bacteria were stopped by penicillin. He found that it can kill the germs that cause scarlet fever, pneumonia, gonorrhea, meningitis, and diphtheria, a roll call of the world's most dangerous infections. Penicillin had the potential of being the ideal antiseptic, provided he could show that it was safe for humans.

A few tests under the microscope convinced him that penicillin does not kill white blood cells (unlike the antiseptics used during World War I). It does not reduce the white cells' ability to swallow bacteria, even when it is present in much larger concentrations than is needed to kill the bacteria themselves. Later, mice and rabbits were injected with the substance and showed no ill effects. The pieces were falling into place.

But there were some disappointments too. Not every bacterium succumbs to penicillin. Typhoid, paratyphoid, and coliform bacteria, for example, are immune to it.

Penicillin is a slow-acting antiseptic. It has to be prepared in advance and placed in the culture dish before the bacteria begin to grow. Then when the culture is incubated at body temperature, the penicillin kills them gradually, as they are dividing. It takes four or five hours for the penicillin to do its work.

In Fleming's hands, penicillin proved to be quite unstable. Stored at room temperature, it lost most of its potency over a period of a week or two. For clinical tests, there could almost never be a fresh batch ready at the same time that there was a suitable patient to try it on. The presence of blood serum seemed to sharply decrease penicillin's potency. This would argue against its being useful when injected into patients. Penicillin decomposes at high temperatures. This makes it more difficult to work with it chemically.

The next step was to try to separate and purify penicillin. Fleming found that he could make a good preparation by growing the mold in a meat broth nutrient for a few days at room temperature. Then he would filter the broth to remove solids, including the mold itself. This "mold juice filtrate" was the source of the penicillin used in most of Fleming's experiments. To go any farther, he needed help.

At this point Fleming assigned two young researchers to

try to concentrate the active ingredient: Dr. Stuart Craddock, the research scholar who had used his laboratory during the summer vacation, and Dr. Frederick Ridley, an ophthalmologist with some training in biochemistry. The conditions under which Ridley and Craddock worked were crude. They had no laboratory of their own but used tables set up in the hallway. The vacuum pump at their disposal was primitive. Nevertheless, in the four months that they worked on the project, they made good progress.

The mold filtrate containing the penicillin is mostly water. One way to concentrate the penicillin is to boil off the water. But at the normal boiling point, 100° Centigrade, penicillin decomposes. As anyone who has camped at high altitudes knows, the boiling point of water can be lowered by reducing the pressure. Ridley and Craddock used a vacuum pump to help make the water boil at only 40° C, just a little above body temperature. After all the water evaporated, the sticky mass that was left included all the germ-killing activity.

Craddock and Ridley also found that penicillin was soluble in alcohol. Dissolved in water, it could be made more stable if the solution was made slightly acidic. In a short time these two were able to produce more concentrated, though by no means pure, samples of penicillin that Fleming could use in his experiments with bacteria.

In the meantime Fleming became fascinated by one of the microbes that penicillin didn't kill. This was the bacillus *Haemophilus influenzae*, also known as Pfeiffer's bacillus. Despite its name, *H. influenzae* does not cause influenza, which is a virus disease. But it merited further attention nevertheless.

The vaccine department of the laboratory wanted to grow Pfeiffer's bacillus so they could produce vaccines for it. But it was a difficult germ to grow. Throat swabs from sick patients, which might be expected to contain some influenza bacillus, were usually accompanied by several other kinds of germs that grew faster in culture than *H. influenzae.* Faced with such competition, the influenza bacillus often did not grow at all. The task of growing pure cultures of Pfeiffer's bacillus had given the laboratory staff many headaches.

Penicillin provided the answer to the problem. It could kill or prevent the growth of most of the competing species. In order to grow a pure culture of the influenza bacillus, Fleming needed only to cover the culture dish with penicillin before implanting the bacteria. The "differential culture" thus produced was a neat solution to a tough laboratory problem.

And so the first applied use of penicillin was, ironically, to promote the growth of a bacteria that is insensitive to the drug. Fleming was proud of this technical achievement. In the talks he gave and in the papers he published, he placed a great deal of emphasis on the use of penicillin to isolate the influenza bacillus. For the next ten years the principal use of Fleming's discovery was a bacteriological "weed killer" to enhance the cultivation and study of an elusive bacillus that may or may not have been the cause of any important human disease.

The announcement of the discovery of penicillin was made at a lecture at the Medical Research Club on February 13, 1929. The publication of the results appeared in the issue of May 10, 1929, of the *British Journal of Experimental Pathology.* The paper described the powerful antibacterial action of the new reagent, and Fleming speculated on its use as an antiseptic. But in neither that paper nor any publications that followed in the next decade, did he report any great clinical success in its use.

And then, strangely, the work came to a halt. Ridley and Craddock left the laboratory and went their separate ways. Fleming tried his weak preparations of penicillin as an antiseptic on some open wounds in clinical patients, with indifferent results. He made no attempt to administer penicillin internally to clinic patients or even to sick animals.

He was probably discouraged by the evidence that blood serum reduces the activity of penicillin. Dr. Craddock had also found that when penicillin was injected into a rabbit, it disappeared from the bloodstream within thirty minutes. If penicillin requires four hours to kill germs, how could it possibly be effective when eliminated in half an hour?

There was only one immediate attempt by scientists outside St. Mary's to follow up on Fleming's discovery. Dr. Harold Raistrick, a biochemist at the London School of Hygiene, read Fleming's paper, obtained a sample of the *penicillium* mold, and went over some of the same ground as Ridley and Craddock. It was Raistrick who sent a sample to Thom in America, leading to the correct identification of *P. notatum*. When Raistrick's group reached an impasse, all research in the world on the isolation of pure penicillin came to a stop.

The fact that a great discovery had been made, but that its development then ceased for ten years, makes a very different story from the others in this volume. How could it have happened? Why did it take the world so long to recognize the miracle that was penicillin? Why didn't Fleming himself continue to pursue the project vigorously? These questions cannot be answered with certainty.

Part of the explanation lies in the lack of resources at St. Mary's. The equipment available was not adequate to the task. The medical doctors and bacteriologists in the research laboratory were not expert chemists and had already done as much as they could with their limited techniques. But there were other laboratories in England and elsewhere where the work could have been done, if not at the universities and hospitals, then in the well-established pharmaceutical industry. For some reason none of them, with the single exception of Raistrick, took up the challenge.

It can be argued that Dr. Fleming did not have the persuasive personality to inspire others to take up where he had shown the way. But the director of the laboratory, Sir Almroth Wright, was certainly capable of making emotional appeals, as he had once done to persuade the army to inoculate its troops with typhoid vaccine before sending them into battle. If he had been convinced that patients were needlessly dying for lack of penicillin, he could certainly have campaigned effectively for its development.

Part of the answer is that Fleming, like any researcher, always had several promising lines of investigation before him. He was always busy—vaccine production to supervise, books to write, a major relocation of the laboratory to plan—and did not have enough resources to follow every possibility. He probably judged that he had done all he could with penicillin, and it was now time to pursue other directions. His results were published where anyone could read them. He made sure his penicillin strain was kept alive for the differential culture work. He readily shared it with anybody who asked. What more could he have done?

The world around him was entering some desperate times. The great depression of the 1930s hit especially hard in Britain. When the concern of every person and every institution was centered on simple economic survival, the practice of research, even when it dealt with life-and-death matters like disease and its cure, must have seemed a great luxury.

On the continent, totalitarian governments had come to

power. Soon a stream of refugees from their cruelty would be flowing westward. And after that there was the specter of war.

Fortunately for humankind, the story of penicillin did not end with Fleming's work. One of the important changes in medicine that took place during the 1930s was the discovery and use of the sulfa drugs, chemicals that can be administered internally and will actually kill or at least inhibit bacteria. The success of these drugs alerted the medical community to the idea that safe chemical antiseptics were not only possible, but that they really existed.

The unsung heroes of the penicillin story are the group of pathologists at Oxford University led by Dr. Howard Florey, an Australian, and Dr. Ernst B. Chain, a Jewish refugee from Germany. In 1938 they undertook a survey of the scientific literature for all the antibacterial agents that had been reported, hoping to find something as effective as the sulfa drugs against a possibly wider range of diseases. Fleming's penicillin featured prominently on their list. Not only was it a very promising germ killer, but it was available in their own laboratory. Descendants of Fleming's mold strain were being carefully tended and grown for their use as a reagent to purify influenza bacillus.

The story of the Oxford work would fill a chapter longer than the one we have already written. Here we have room only to summarize their major achievements. They learned how to concentrate the penicillin and to keep it stable. They found that mice infected with deadly pneumonia were miraculously cured by penicillin. It was an experiment that Fleming might have been able to do, but he had not tried.

After this discovery the Oxford workers learned how to mass-produce penicillin until they had enough of it to test on human patients. By this time World War II had started, and bombs were falling on English cities. The work was transferred to chemical plants in the United States, which were able to produce enough penicillin to save the lives of thousands of wounded soldiers.

In peacetime the drug has been made available to wipe out the threat of diseases like pneumonia and scarlet fever. All of us have almost certainly made use of penicillin or some of the other antibiotics that have followed in its wake.

In December 1945, Fleming, Florey, and Chain shared the Nobel prize in medicine, Fleming for the discovery, Florey and Chain for the development of penicillin. The revolution in medical practice that these men began is still continuing.

# 4. The Echo of the Big Bang: *Cosmic Microwave Background Radiation*

Setting:      1964–1965
              *Bell Telephone Laboratories*
              *Crawford Hill, New Jersey.*
Protagonists: Arno A. Penzias, 31
              Robert W. Wilson, 29
              *radio astronomers*

*Two young scientists, using the big radio antenna at Bell Labs to look for weak signals from the sky, were having trouble getting rid of the background noise. They tried vainly to clean up their apparatus, blaming the noise on everything from pigeon droppings to nuclear weapons tests. The background noise did not go away, and they were honest enough to admit they could not explain where it was coming from.*

*If this had happened a few years earlier, their efforts might have passed unnoticed as just another failed experiment. But in 1964 some theoretical astrophysicists were beginning to take seriously the Big Bang model of the universe, the idea that the universe began in a great explosion about fifteen billion years ago. Calculations showed that the echos of that great outburst should still be ringing around the world in the form of a weak radio signal that could be detected with an antenna like the one at Crawford Hill.*

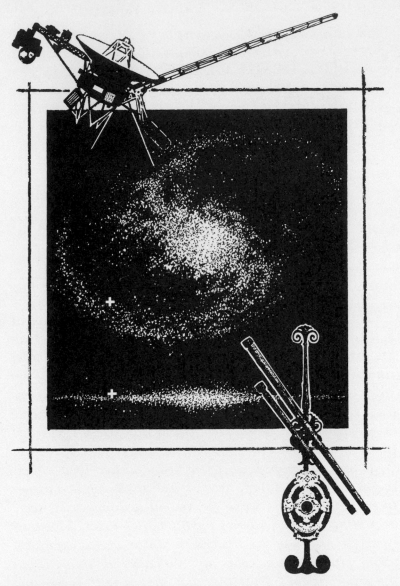

Arno Penzias and Robert Wilson set out to find radio signals coming from our galaxy, a spiral-armed collection of billions of stars. It was one step in the human exploration of space that began with Galileo's telescope (*lower right*) and continues with the Voyager spacecraft (*upper left*).

*The calculation had been done before, as early as 1948, but it had been ignored or forgotten. This time the word got through from the theoreticians to the experimenters, from Princeton to Crawford Hill—twenty-five miles, as the crow flies—by way of Baltimore and Cambridge, Massachusetts. Penzias and Wilson learned that they had been listening to the oldest radio broadcast in history.*

Go out and look at the sky on a clear, dark night. The heavens sparkle with the light from thousands of stars, each shining as brightly as our own sun. You should be able to recognize a swath of light, a thin glowing cloud, as the Milky Way. A telescope, even a good pair of binoculars, shows us that this glowing patch is made up of millions of stars shining together, so close that the naked eye cannot distinguish them. They appear instead as a continuous streak of light.

Why isn't the whole sky like that?

This question occurred to William Olbers, an amateur astronomer who lived two hundred years ago. If the number of stars were really infinite, Olbers argued, the whole night sky should be bright with their light.

The farther away a star is, the dimmer the light that reaches us. But there are more of them farther away. Their numbers increase in just the right way to cancel their individual dimness. If there is no end to the stars, the sky should be blazing with the sum of all their brilliances.

Our senses tell us this is not the case. Even the Milky Way, when we look at it through a telescope, reveals darkness between the stars. Olbers concluded that the universe is not infinite, that eventually there is a place where the stars come to an end. But that is not the only possible explanation.

We realize today that the stars are so far away that it

takes a long time for their light to reach us. We see them not as they are now, but as they were thousands and millions of years ago, when the light beams were just setting out on the long journey from the star to our eyes. Looking out at the sky is like looking far back in time.

There may have been a time long ago when there were no stars shining. This possibility would answer Olbers's question in a different way. The number of stars we can see is finite, since the light from the more distant ones has not yet had time to reach us since they first began to glow.

This idea leads to an important consequence. It says that the universe was not always the way it is now. It implies that the world had a beginning.

What Olbers could not have anticipated, what astronomers well into the middle of the twentieth century did not realize, is that the sky *is* uniformly bright, and always has been. Not at the wavelengths of light that the eye can see, but in a much different part of the spectrum.

That discovery belongs to two young physicists working for Bell Telephone Laboratories in New Jersey. On average over the years they spent half their time working on problems relevant to telephone communication, and the other half doing radio astronomy. In 1963 they were working on radio astronomy.

The whole idea of radio astronomy had been established at Bell Telephone Labs thirty years earlier. In 1934 Karl Jansky, a radio engineer, had been assigned to find out the sources of all the radio noise in the airwaves. He had determined that a significant fraction of it was coming from the direction of the center of the Milky Way. Jansky's major clue was that this radio source crosses the sky four minutes earlier each day, just as all the stars do, because of the earth's motion around the sun.

The discovery that the stars emit radio waves is itself an example of serendipity. But Jansky and Bell Labs hadn't followed up on this discovery. During the Depression, they had more practical problems to solve. Only after World War II, during which great improvements in radio and microwave equipment had been made, did radio astronomy begin to develop.

In the early 1960s Bell Labs thought they might get back into the radio astronomy business. Their communications engineers had built a twenty-foot horn reflector antenna at Crawford Hill, New Jersey, to receive signals bounced off the Echo satellite. That project was now over. It seemed wasteful to let a receiver with such excellent characteristics lie unused.

Arno Penzias, who had emigrated at age six from Germany with his family, had come to work at Bell Labs after getting his Ph.D. degree at Columbia University. There he had built a maser, a low-noise microwave amplifier of the type invented by his thesis sponsor, Charles Townes. Penzias had used the maser in conjunction with a radio telescope.

Texas-born Robert Woodrow Wilson was an astrophysicist who had just completed his thesis at California Institute of Technology ("Caltech") in Pasadena. Both of these scientists were under thirty when they started work at Bell Labs, and neither had a great scientific reputation.

At Caltech, Wilson had taken a course given by the British astrophysicist, Fred Hoyle. Hoyle was promoting a model of the universe known as the "steady-state" cosmology. According to Hoyle, the universe has no beginning and no end; it was always just about the way it is now. In this model, the galaxies were flying apart from each other, and new matter was being created to fill the gap. The newly created matter would soon coalesce to form new galaxies. The older galaxies would speed away from each other, eventually receding so fast that their light could never reach us. This was another way to explain Olbers's paradox.

The rate of creation needed to sustain the steady state is so tiny that we could never hope to detect it. "One neutron in the volume of the Cavendish Laboratory in the lifetime of a Cavendish professor," as Cambridge-educated Hoyle put it, was enough to keep things going nicely.

If Robert Wilson had been asked in 1963 which model of the world he favored, he would have endorsed the steady-state idea that he learned from Hoyle at Caltech. The discovery he and Penzias were about to make turned out to be the death blow for that theory.

Penzias's Ph.D. thesis had involved a search for atomic hydrogen between the stars. He wanted to see how empty interstellar space really was. He hadn't found any then, but he expected that with better equipment a repeated search might be successful.

You don't expect to find hydrogen atoms on the stars themselves; stars are so hot that the electrons are stripped off the atoms as soon as they are formed by the violent collisions constantly taking place. The place to look for stable hydrogen atoms is in directions where there are few stars, away from the center of the Milky Way, in the "halo" of our galaxy.

Wilson had had some experience at Caltech mapping out radio waves coming from the center of the galaxy. The technique was simple; you never had to measure the absolute level of any radio signal, only the relative strength of signals compared with one another. In a typical experiment the antenna would be pointed in a direction where there were no radio sources. Whatever signal level that was detected was considered background noise. If the antenna was left alone, the background would not be expected to change. Then as the hours wore on, the earth's rotation would swing the Milky Way across the viewing field of the antenna. The signal level would go up. The increase in intensity over the background measured earlier (and later) could be due only to the radio source source in the galaxy. It was a neat way to subtract the background and thereby measure the relative intensity of the radio signals coming from the Milky Way.

This technique does not work in the search for radio sources in the halo of the galaxy that surrounds us. These sources would be equally strong in all directions. In essence, we are *inside* the source. There is no way to turn it off.

Penzias was convinced that he could solve this problem. His idea was to build a noise-free detector, or at least one with the very minimum of background. The horn reflector at Crawford Hill was already close to what was needed. It was capable of picking up the very weak signals that had been reflected from the Echo satellite. The engineers reported that the noise level, though very low, was a bit higher than they had expected. Penzias knew a few ways to improve its performance. With some luck and more hard work, he hoped to achieve the ultimate, a completely noise-free radio telescope. With no background noise, he would not have to settle for measuring the relative intensity of radio signals. He could measure instead their absolute intensity.

It is common for radio engineers to express the level of radio noise—or radio signals—in terms of an equivalent temperature. This measure is based on the nineteenth-century discovery that the radiation inside an oven (or any other enclosed cavity) is determined completely by its temperature. It is the same no matter what the size or shape of the cavity, what the walls are made of, or what (if anything) is inside it.

At a temperature of a few hundred degrees above room

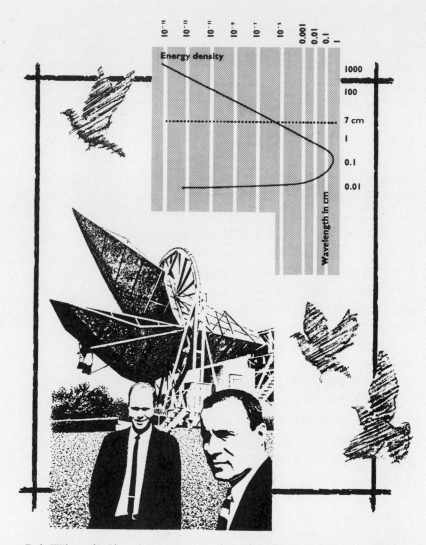

Bob Wilson (*left*) and Arno Penzias (*right*) in front of the horn reflector radio telescope, which was troubled by the intrusion of a family of pigeons. The spectrum of radio noise that they could not get rid of fits the curve one would expect inside an oven cooking at three degrees above absolute zero (*top center*).

temperature, an oven glows red hot. At a few thousand degrees it is blazing white. At room temperature an oven is filled with infrared radiation not visible to our eyes but measurable with the right equipment. At temperatures far below that, an oven is dominated by radio and microwaves. (Microwaves are the part of the radio spectrum with frequencies above the UHF television band.)

The intensity of a radio source can be characterized by its equivalent temperature. A relatively high temperature describes a bright, or noisy (the words mean the same thing in this context) radio star. The galactic halo that Penzias and Wilson wanted to measure was expected to be very dim. It could be estimated to raise the level of radio noise by only about one degree.

The receiver at Crawford Hill was behaving as if it were in a cavity at a very low temperature. The so-called antenna temperature was only a few degrees above absolute zero ($-273°$ C, or $-460°$ F). It was a very quiet antenna indeed. But, for the purposes of Penzias and Wilson, it was not quiet enough.

There was a lot of cleaning up to do. The antenna and its connected circuits had to be rewired to get rid of all the stray sources of noise that they could think of. In the end, what background could not be eliminated would have to be measured. Then the measured background could be subtracted from the signal they received. The difference would be the true radio intensity from the galaxy.

The detected signal was expected to come from three sources. There was the noise from the receiver electronics, which they were trying so hard to reduce. There was the background noise from the earth, the atmosphere, nearby cities, and radar stations. And there was the signal from the sky itself.

To help subtract the contribution of the receiver, Penzias

built a "cold load," a mock antenna that was cooled with liquid helium, which could be kept at a temperature five Celsius degrees above absolute zero (or 5° Kelvin). The cold load could be expected to have a low but well-understood noise level. Wilson built a switch so that the receiver circuits could be connected alternately to the cold load and then to the antenna. Any difference would have to be coming from the antenna itself.

The effect of the earth's atmosphere could be measured by pointing the antenna close to the horizon, where its effect is highly exaggerated, and then straight overhead, where you are looking at the shortest possible column of atmosphere. The radio noise coming from the air directly above them was calculated to be equivalent to an antenna temperature of 2.3° Kelvin. Even with the antenna pointed straight up, it was their largest known source of background.

Radar signals could be identified because they come in short bursts, not the steady stream of static that astronomical sources usually produce. They were careful not to take data on days when nearby radar installations were active.

The general radio noise generated by civilization might have been a factor. They pointed the antenna toward New York City, fifty miles away, and picked up a signal. Its intensity was about what was expected, and dropped off rapidly when the antenna was pointed elsewhere. Altogether the contribution from the ground, when the antenna was aimed overhead, was calculated to be negligible.

It was reasonable to expect that the real antenna, pointed straight up, should produce less static than the cold load. In terms of equivalent temperature, the cold load was 5° Kelvin. The background sources they could account for, coming through the real antenna, amounted to no more than 3.5° K.

In fact, the antenna was noisier than the cold load. It was behaving as if it were in an enclosure at 7° Kelvin. This was not good enough for the experiments Penzias and Wilson wanted to do. The signal they wanted to detect from the galaxy was estimated to contribute only one degree to the antenna temperature. Before they could begin to measure such a low-level signal, they would have to understand all the backgrounds very much better.

Their intention was to tune the receiver eventually to a wavelength of 21 centimeters. That is the characteristice wavelength of the hydrogen atom. It is the wavelength at which this atom broadcasts when the spins of its electron and proton are disturbed. But they hadn't made this major change in the receiver yet. They also intended to do some work at 22 centimeters, to investigate the radio signal not associated with any particular atom. (In fact, given the outcome of this experiment, they never did get to look at 22 centimeters.) At the time they were operating at 7.35 centimeters, the wavelength that had been used by the communications engineers who worked on the antenna before them.

This wavelength corresponds to a frequency of 4.08 Gigahertz, 4.08 billion cycles per second. (The product of wavelength times frequency is just the speed of light—or in this case, the speed of radio waves—30 billion centimeters per second.) It is a frequency at which the radio noise from our galaxy is expected to be low.

One can check this fact by doing an ordinary radio scan of any nearby galaxy, such as the great nebula in Andromeda. These galaxies exhibit no particular signal as they move across the field of a radio telescope tuned to 4 Gigahertz frequency. If our own galaxy is anything like the ones around it, it should also be quiet at 4 Gigahertz.

So the 4 Gigahertz frequency was an excellent place to check the cleanness of the radio receiver. No radio signal from any stellar source was expected there. Once Penzias and Wilson had accounted for all the backgrounds at that frequency, they could go on to measure the real signals— if they existed—at 21 centimeters.

At the moment they were finding an unaccounted 3 to 4 degree excess background that was driving them wild.

The continuous-creation model of the universe, which was favored by many astronomers in the 1950s, accounted neatly for one of the major observations about distant galaxies. In 1929 Edwin Hubble had announced that all but the nearest galaxies seemed to be flying away from us at high speeds. The farther away the galaxy, the more rapidly it is receding.

According to the steady-state theory, the space being evacuated by the fleeing galaxies was being filled with newly created matter. The alternative to this model was derided by Fred Hoyle as the "Big Bang" model. According to the latter idea, a great cosmic explosion about fifteen billion years ago had started all the galaxies in motion away from each other. The ones that had started off fastest—relative to us—would now be the farthest away. That would explain Hubble's observations. But it would involve a concept of the early universe that people like Hoyle found mind-bogging.

If you take the Big Bang model seriously you have to conclude that at one time the world was very different than we see it today. It would mean that once all the stars, all the galaxies, all the matter in the universe was very much closer together than it is now. If you follow the Big Bang idea to its logical extreme, you envision an era in which all the atoms and their nuclei that now exists were packed so tightly that their density exceeded that of the centers of any star today. This inconceivably dense plasma must have filled all space, everywhere, at that moment. What had happened before that, to cause the explosion, is almost beyond conjecture.

At least one group of theoretical astrophysicists had taken the Big Bang model seriously. George Gamow, at George Washington University, his former student, Ralph Alpher, and their colleague, Robert Herman, had published a calculation back in 1948.

Gamow, Alpher, and Herman began with the observation that there is still a lot of hydrogen in the world. Our sun and most stars get their energy today by combining hydrogen nuclei, protons, to form helium.

If, at the time of creation, the protons were all squeezed together close enough to touch each other, why didn't they react quickly to form nuclei of all the heavier elements? There shouldn't be any single protons left to fuel the stars today.

The way out of this problem, as Gamow and his colleagues saw it, was that the Big Bang had to be very hot, so hot that collisions between rapidly moving particles would break up any nucleus as soon as it was formed. Such a hot universe would be full of blazing radiation: ultraviolet waves, X rays, gamma rays. All of it would shine with blinding intensity equally in all directions, constantly being absorbed and re-emitted by the dense, hot nuclear matter that filled all space.

The universe then expanded and cooled off as it did so. The protons combined with electrons to form hydrogen atoms. As billions of years passed, the swirling gases clumped together to form galaxies, stars within those galaxies, and planets in orbit around some of those stars. On at least one of those planets, living creatures evolved, and intelligence and civilization as we know it came into being.

What happened to the brilliant radiation that was shining at the time of the Big Bang? If the laws of physics have not changed in all that time, it should still be around! As the world has gotten bigger, the wavelengths should have gotten longer. As the volume of space to be filled has increased, the energy of the radiation has had to be spread thinner. Gamma rays have now become radio waves. Radiation temperatures once reckoned in millions of degrees have now dropped to near absolute zero.

But the radiation should still be there, still coming at us from all directions. If the heavens are not blazing bright, they are at least shining at a low but uniform rate all over the sky. The waves that we receive today started out at some far corners of the Big Bang, and have only now managed to reach us. Light that was emitted from *our* region of the universe back then is finally arriving, much attenuated, at stars so far away we cannot see them yet.

Gamow, Alpher, and Herman calculated in 1948 that the radiation from the Big Bang should leave a residue in our vicinity now, equivalent to a temperature of 5° Kelvin. It is a remarkably close prediction to the value eventuallly observed, 2.7° K. But these theoreticians did not think that such a low level of radio noise was actually observable. Over the next few years they continued to refine their calculations, but by 1953 they had dropped this line of reasoning and had gone their separate ways.

None of the principal people working on the problem ten years later, not experimentalists like Penzias and Wilson, nor theoreticians like Fred Hoyle, had read or heard of the work of Gamow, Alpher, and Herman.

At Crawford Hill, the two young scientists continued to search for the sources of noise. They discovered that some pigeons were making their nest inside the antenna horn and suspected that the pigeon droppings were degrading the electrical properties of the telescope.

The pigeons were caught and shipped off to another site. They returned, were trapped again, and disposed of permanently. The antenna was taken apart and cleaned out. This helped some but not enough. Every possible joint and crack was sealed with aluminum tape, using electrically conducting glue, to prevent the leakage of noise into the horn. None of this electrical work made any improvement.

At one point they suspected that recent nuclear testing in the atmosphere might be contributing to the microwave noise. A bomb exploded in the upper stratosphere would send streams of electrons into orbits high overhead, which might be the source of radio waves from above. Then in 1963 a limited nuclear test ban became effective. There would be no more weapons exploded above ground by Americans or Russians. The electrons in orbit should gradually be disappearing, and with them the radio noise they create. The noise in the Crawford Hill antenna showed no sign of diminishing.

By 1964 some theoreticians were rediscovering for themselves the work of Gamow, Alpher, and Herman. Fred Hoyle himself, with R. J. Tayler, published a paper on the topic. A Russian named Yakov B. Zeldovich went even farther. In an article reviewing work by other Russians, he quoted experimental evidence to show that the microwave background was much less than the Big Bang model would predict. Ironically, the data he used was derived from the same twenty-foot horn antenna that Penzias and Wilson and Wilson were now using! The communications engineers working on Echo satellite reflections had reported on the performance of the antenna in 1961. The Russians had misunderstood the article and thought that it set an upper limit of 1° K. on the radiation temperature, whereas the Big Bang model would predict several degrees. The Russian article was translated into English, but apparently no Americans noticed it.

Independently of all these others, physicists at Princeton University were working on some of the same ideas. Professor Robert H. Dicke, working on his own idea of an "oscillating universe"—a universe that went through repeated cycles of expansion and contraction—suggested to his colleague, P. J. E. "Jim" Peebles, that Peebles calculate how hot the Big Bang must have been. In 1946 Dicke had worked on a microwave project that set an upper limit of 20° Kelvin for the microwave background level. Twenty years later, even Dicke had forgotten this result.

Peebles came up with the calculation that the present-day microwave background could be ten degrees. If that were so, it might be detectable with modern equipment. Dicke suggested to two young colleagues, Peter G. Roll and David T. Wilkinson, that they search for these microwaves. Roll and Wilkinson set up a receiver on the roof of the physics building and began searching.

In early 1965, Peebles gave a talk about his calculations at the physics department of Johns Hopkins University in Baltimore. In the audience was Ken Turner of Carnegie Institution, who was so impressed by the lecture that he mentioned it to his colleague, Bernard Burke, a radio astronomer at MIT.

One is reminded of the lyrics by the comic songwriter,

Tom Lehrer: "I have a friend in Minsk, who has a friend in Pinsk. . . ." Science news can travel at high speeds, but sometimes by roundabout routes.

Penzias just happened to call his friend Burke for reasons unrelated to the project at hand. Burke knew about the Crawford Hill radio telescope work. At the end of the conversation, he asked Penzias how the work was coming along. Penzias admitted that he was still having trouble understanding the noise background. Burke suggested that he call the physicists at Princeton, who might have some ideas to share with him.

It is only a short drive from Princeton to the Bell Laboratories center in Holmdel, New Jersey. Dicke, Roll, and Wilkinson came over together. Penzias and Wilson showed the Princeton people their data and listened patiently to the cosmological explanation. It must have been staggering to contemplate that the radio signals they were receiving might have been in transit for fifteen billion years. The message they carried was revolutionary: the Big Bang theory now had supporting evidence.

The facts were becoming clear. The noise in the Crawford Hill antenna was real. It would not go away. It could not be eliminated. It could not be accounted for by any known source. It must be coming from the sky.

Since the noise was the same, no matter which part of the heavens was overhead, it could not be coming from any single star or cluster. It was not likely to be coming from the galaxy as a whole, since no other galaxy emitted radiation at that wavelength. The source of the background noise was larger than any galaxy, possibly as large as the universe itself. In effect, the Crawford Hill telescope is in a large oven, an oven as big as the universe, at a temperature of three degrees above absolute zero.

The implications were stunning. The Big Bang had really happened. The universe had a beginning. It is "only" about fifteen billion years old. Before that time there had been . . . nothing.

Penzias and Wilson were not at first convinced of the Princeton group's explanation. It was nice, they felt, to have some theory that accounted for what they were seeing, but it might not be the only explanation for their observations. Perhaps the steady-state advocates could still come up with an answer. Penzias and Wilson certainly did not want to claim that the Big-Bang explanation was their own idea.

They decided to be cautious about what they said for publication. The paper, which appeared in the *Astrophysical Journal*, was titled "A Measurement of Excess Antenna Temperature at 4,080 Mc/s." They reported that the effective noise temperature directly overhead was about 3.5° higher than they could account for with any known combination of astronomical sources. There was no mention of any possible explanation of this effect, except to refer to the paper by Dicke, Peebles, Roll, and Wilkinson, which followed immediately after theirs in the same issue of the journal.

Confirmation was quick in coming. Roll and Wilkinson completed their measurements and reported finding the same 3° Kelvin noise level at a radio wavelength of 3.2 centimeters. Other radio astronomers reported 3° temperature at wavelengths ranging from seventy centimeters down to a few millimeters. The combination of all these results was to show that the shape of the microwave background spectrum was exactly what was to be expected for an oven at a fixed temperature, namely 3° Kelvin. There could be no doubt that they were measuring the temperature of a very large microwave cavity. In effect, what was being determined was the absolute temperature of the whole world, the absolute level of radiation in the universe.

While recognition of the significance of this discovery was building in the astrophysics community, Bell Labs pursued other interests. While Penzias and Wilson continued to work in radio astronomy part-time, much of their activity was directed into lines of research of more immediate use to the telephone company. Later in their careers, both were able to return to radio astronomy. They did important work, discovering molecules like carbon monoxide in the clouds between the stars. The follow-up on the cosmic microwave background radiation has mostly been done by others.

As late as 1972, a book publicizing the work at Bell Labs, intended for the general public, made no mention of Penzias and Wilson. Arthur Gregor's *Bell Laboratories: Inside the World's Largest Communications Center* (New York: Charles Scribner's Sons, 1972) is full of references to such great Bell Labs inventions as the transistor and the video telephone. The book mentions both Karl Jansky's discovery of radio astronomy and communications using the Echo satellite. But Bell Laboratories' public relations and administration departments, which cooperated in gathering information and illustrations for the book, did not call the writer's attention to the cosmic discovery announced by two of its young scientists in 1965.

In 1978 Penzias and Wilson received the Nobel prize in physics. More recent histories of the laboratory feature their names more prominently.

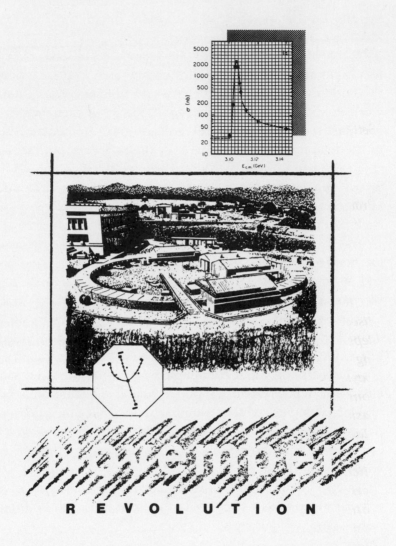

With mounting excitement, Burton Richter's group of experimenters at the SPEAR facility (*center*) at Stanford traced out the curve (*upper right*) of annihilation rate versus beam energy with the sharp peak that marked the presence of what they named the Psi meson. The disintegration of the psi-prime into four charged particles (*lower left*) seems to spell out the Greek letter psi.

# 5. The November Revolution: Discovery of the J/Psi Meson

Setting:        November 1974
                Brookhaven National Laboratory, Long Island,
                New York
                Stanford Linear Accelerator Center, California
Protagonists:   Samuel C. C. Ting, 38,
                Professor of Physics, MIT
                Burton C. Richter, 43,
                Professor at SLAC

*It sometimes happens that two scientists make the same discovery at about the same time, working completely independently of each other. This is usually explained by saying that the idea was "in the air." New techniques, new ways of thinking develop to the point that a discovery becomes inevitable. We should not be surprised that it occasionally happens almost simultaneously in two or more places.*

*This sort of double discovery is less likely in the complicated world of subnuclear particle physics. Particle experiments take years to set up and large numbers of scientists to carry out. They are done in the bright spotlight of national laboratories, where potential competitors are watching over researchers' shoulders. In such a setting, how could an important discovery not become general knowledge long before any rival has time to build the apparatus to duplicate the work?*

*And yet it happened! The group led by Burton C. Richter*

*at Stanford, in an atmosphere of rising excitement, was finding what they named the Psi meson, on the very day that Samuel Ting arrived in California prepared to announce his own group's discovery at Brookhaven of what he christened the J particle. When notes were compared, it became obvious that the J and the Psi were the same object.*

*The graphs that both groups presented were strikingly similar, the kind of curve that quickens the pulse rate of any particle physicist. There was a sharp, narrow peak projecting upward above a smooth, slowly varying background. It signaled the presence of a short-lived, well-defined subnuclear particle known as a meson.*

*Ting had driven his MIT-based group to set up experiments at laboratories in three countries, hoping to detect such a meson as it disintegrated into an electron plus a positron. Richter's group had stumbled across the same particle using the reverse reaction, making electrons and positrons collide at just the right energy to form the new meson.*

*Was it serendipity? Ting, for reasons best known to himself, had delayed announcing what his group had found. He then suspected that the news had leaked out and that the Stanford group was following up an inside tip. Richter's people, however, were reinvestigating some anomalous data points that they had noticed several months previously, before Ting's experiment had even begun operation. The Stanford group had been amazed to see the prominent mesonic peak rise up over the broad plain of data they had traversed so many times before.*

*The J/Psi meson is the Rosetta stone of subnuclear physics, the key to understanding everything else. The quark model, which says that all the subnuclear particles such as protons, neutrons, and mesons are made up of a few kinds of small building blocks called quarks, had until then been only a tentative hypothesis. The theory lacked a simple system for which calculations can easily be made and readily checked against experiment. The particle found by Ting's and Richter's group provided that test case. If the meson is treated as a particular quark and corresponding antiquark moving around each other (the way electron and proton circle each other in a hydrogen atom), the details of its behavior can easily be explained. From 1974 on, the quark model was on firm ground.*

*When, ten days after the discovery of the Psi meson, Richter's group at Stanford found the Psi-prime meson, the door was open to a new spectroscopy, the study of all the possible states of this quark-antiquark pair. The events of November 1974, caused a revolution in the thinking of particle physicists. The quark model has emerged as the unchallenged leader in our explanation of subnuclear physics.*

Sometimes it seemed that Professor Samuel C. C. Ting was spending most of his life on airplanes. His research group was working on experiments at three different laboratories: in New York state, in West Germany, and in Switzerland. He had teaching duties at Massachusetts Institute of Technology. And here he was, flying into San Francisco airport on a Sunday afternoon.

He rented a car for the thirty-minute drive to Palo Alto. The gasoline crisis of 1974 had subsided by November, and there would be no problems with refilling the tank. He had reservations at a hotel near the campus of Stanford University.

The next morning there would be a meeting at SLAC, the Stanford Linear Accelerator Center. Some of the world's most prominent high-energy physicists would be there. Ting had some news that was sure to startle them all.

Ting, an American who was brought up in China, had never done any research at SLAC, and he had no plans to begin now. He was a member of the laboratory's Program Advisory Committee.

All the big labs have such a committee. Scientists compete to use the unique and expensive facilities at large labs, and a board of impartial experts is needed to prevent conflicts. The committee consists of leading scientists, mostly from outside the lab, who consider proposals and make recommendations about which experiments should be scheduled. As a well-known outside scientist who had no designs of his own to do experiments at Stanford, Ting was a good choice to be an arbiter at SLAC.

The main feature of the SLAC laboratory is a two-mile-long evacuated pipe, fitted with electrical devices to accelerate electrons up to nearly the speed of light. The building that houses it, one of the longest enclosed structures in the world, is visible on satellite photos of the San Francisco Bay area. The freeway that crosses over it and the San Andreas earthquake fault that passes close by have not affected the reliable operation of this accelerator.

For more than a year, a smaller facility had also been operating, called the Stanford Positron/Electron Accelerating Ring (SPEAR). SPEAR is the brainchild of Professor Burton Richter, a Brooklyn-born extrovert who had come to Stanford by way of MIT. The SPEAR ring receives high-energy electrons and positrons from the main accelerator and uses magnetic fields to keep them circulating in opposite directions around the ring. Occasionally one electron and one positron annihilate each other, a spectacular event on a subatomic scale. The details of these annihilations are the subjects of research at SPEAR.

The program committee meeting was scheduled for Monday, November 11, 1974, so that some outside members arriving from a distance could take advantage of the Veterans' Day holiday. It came just as the Stanford accelerators were coming back to life after a four-month extended summer shutdown. The agenda was to be the approval of new experiments and the extension of existing ones, using both the main accelerated beam and the SPEAR facility.

Ting had a surprise ready for the committee. He was about to make the first public announcement of a new discovery by his research group. Working at Brookhaven National Laboratory, on Long Island, New York, they had observed a new subnuclear particle, very different from any that been found before. Its mass was unusually high, more than three times as much as a proton. Although it disintegrates almost as soon as it is produced—like most such unstable subnuclear particles—its lifetime seems nevertheless to be unexpectedly long for such a massive particle.

At Brookhaven the new particle had been seen to split into an electron-positron pair. At SPEAR, Ting expected, the opposite reaction should be possible. If an electron and a positron collide at exactly the right energy, they ought to be able to form the new particle. Finding the correct energy would normally involve a difficult search. But with Ting's new results, the SPEAR experimenters would know just where to look. Using this revelation, SPEAR could begin its second year of operation with an elegant confirmation of the Ting group's discovery. With the happy prospect of a triumphant disclosure at tomorrow's meeting in mind, Ting checked into his hotel.

There was a message waiting at the desk to call Professor Martin Deutsch back home in Cambridge. There were always messages like that waiting. Ting moved around a lot, and his colleagues had to work hard to keep up communications with him. May as well return the call now, he thought, before it gets too late in Massachusetts.

Deutsch reported that he had heard rumors of a lot of excitement going on at SPEAR. He didn't know exactly what it was about, but it had stirred up enough telephone traffic to make an impact three thousand miles away on a Sunday afternoon.

Ting had a suspicion. They have found my particle, he thought. How could they have known where to look? Did the information leak out? Here he had been holding back his results, waiting for the right moment to announce them. And now this has happened.

Scientists at the forefront don't expect to make money by selling their inventions. Their payoff comes from recognition—honors, promotions, support for further research—that follows from being the first to report new discoveries. The priority is to publish the news as soon as one is certain that the conclusions are correct.

Anyway, the results of research cannot be kept secret for long. Teams of scientists work together in large laboratories, constantly discussing each other's work. Progress reports have to be made regularly in order to justify next year's funding and to gain or prolong access to special expensive equipment.

This is especially true in the world of subnuclear particle physics. Because the experiments are so complicated, research teams tend to be large. The more people who share a secret, the harder it is to keep. The high-energy laboratories where this work can be done are few in number. Particle physicists from everywhere else must come to these accelerator centers to do their work. So there is a constant flow of physicists to these laboratories, a constant daily contact among the people active in the field. In this atmosphere, the slightest rumor of any interesting ideas or data can and will be spread around the globe as fast as telephone lines can carry them.

It was time for Ting to generate some telephone traffic of his own. His hotel bill shows several long-distance calls made that evening, particularly to places in the world that might not have heard from Stanford yet. He began by calling people he knew on the SLAC staff. The first one he reached was Dr. Stanley Brodsky, a theoretical physicist who was not directly involved with any experiment. Brodsky was hesitant. He had been talking to Richter and had some idea what was happening at SPEAR, but he wasn't sure what he could reveal to an outsider.

Ting decided to make his claim for priority right then on the telephone to Brodsky, even though he did not know for sure who had found what at SPEAR. Ting began to describe exactly what the results at Brookhaven were: the mass, the lifetime, the disintegration mode of this exciting new particle. Brodsky offered to schedule a special lecture meeting the next day, where Ting could announce his results in public. It was time for the secret to come out.

If any research group in particle physics were capable of keeping information from the outside world, at least for a time, it might have been the American-German group headed by Professor Samuel C. C. Ting. In the late 1960s this team was conducting experiments at the German national electron accelerator, Deutsches Elektronen-Synchrotron, "DESY" for short, at Hamburg. Ting, then still in his early thirties and already a faculty member at Columbia University, was a hard-working, hard-driving, productive group leader.

Ting's group was not large. About a dozen physicists with doctorates worked in the group then, as in 1974. These were joined by a few graduate students who worked with them for a time, used some of the data to write a thesis, and then left. This is almost the minimum number of people needed to keep a high-energy experiment going. The apparatus is elaborate, and many specialists are needed to keep it running around the clock. Two or three physicists are always needed "on shift," and several other experts are on call when data is being taken.

Professor Ting kept his little group under tight control. An illustration of how exacting he could be appears in the rules posted at the experimental "hut" at the DESY laboratory, where physicists monitored the progress of the experiment.

These rules are dated December 16, 1968, over Sam Ting's typewritten signature. It is not certain how long these orders were in force or how well they were obeyed. But they were famous. At high-energy physics laboratories around the world, where collegiality and first-name informality are standard, one can still find copies of Sam Ting's rules posted as examples of how much tougher things could be:

Attention - to all members of E51

The following are the basic understandings which must be followed strictly during shifts. I would like to ask for your collaboration in seeing all these rules maintained during the time of running.

I. Under no circumstances may you switch off any high voltage power supply without talking with me first.

II. Do not change any of the electronics or cables.

III. No newspapers and books of any kind are allowed in the hut.

IV. No food, drinks, coffee, tea, apples, etc. in the hut.

V. No cloths *(sic)*, overcoats, sweaters, and bags of any kind in the hut.

VI. No programming in the hut during shifts.

VII. No private conversations, laugh, and jokes on shift.

VIII. Show up on time and leave on time.....

If Ting was being exacting with his colleagues, he was no less demanding of himself. In the spring of 1970, after five years of continuous work at DESY, as he later wrote, "I became exhausted and on the advice of my physician I took a year off."

At about the same time Ting moved his base from Columbia to the Massachusetts Institute of Technology. Many members of his team transferred with him, the harsh rules for the experimental hut notwithstanding. Most of them would spend little time at M.I.T., as they had spent little at Columbia. The work of an experimental particle physics group is done at the high-energy accelerators, not at the universities where their salaries are paid.

Ting's program for the early 1970s was to set up experiments simultaneously at three different laboratories. They could only run one at a time, but the plan was to concentrate the group's full effort on each one in turn, finish up quickly, and move on to the next. The three laboratories were DESY, scene of their earlier running; Brookhaven National Laboratory, on Long Island; and CERN, an international high-energy physics institution located near Geneva, Switzerland. It was an ambitious program, with a lot of traveling involved, but one they felt capable of carrying out.

The subject of this intense activity was the study of the properties of a class of subatomic particles known as neutral vector mesons. These are an important set of the many new subnuclear objects that have been found in the past half-century.

In 1936, the year Ting was born, it was understood that all normal matter is constructed from just three basic building blocks: protons, neutrons, and electrons. But a generation of experiments with high-energy beams has revealed a much richer underlying structure.

A meson is a piece of subnuclear matter distinguished by its mass and its instability. The name *meson* (from the Greek word for middle) originally implied that it was something whose mass is in between that of electrons and protons. But mesons have since been found that are even heavier than protons. Mesons are now defined by the fact that they quickly disintegrate completely into lighter objects such as electrons. By contrast, the protons in the world have remained intact for as long as the universe has existed.

Many kinds of mesons are known, each with its own distinctive mass, electric charge, and lifetime. Their names are often taken from the Greek alphabet: pi, rho, omega, phi. There are other short-lived nuclear particles that are not mesons; they go by such names as hyperons and leptons. We shall not try to define them here.

Mesons are not found in ordinary matter. They have to be made. They are created from pure energy, proof of Einstein's prediction about the equivalence of mass and energy. The major purpose of the high-energy accelerators around the world is to take some subatomic projectiles—electrons at SLAC and DESY, protons at Brookhaven and CERN—and whirl them up to such high speeds that mesons can be created from their energy. In a typical experiment, a beam of such high-energy projectiles is directed onto a metal target. In collisions between the beam particles and individual nuclei of the target atoms, the various kinds of subnuclear species are born.

One has to act quickly to detect the mesons. Even the longest-lived of them can last no more than a fraction of a microsecond. They cannot be bottled and studied at leisure. The apparatus has to be ready to record their passage in the brief instant before all trace of them has disappeared. The mesons that Ting's group was interested in have lifetimes less than $10^{-22}$ seconds, barely enough time, even traveling at close to the speed of light, to cross the diameter of one atomic nucleus.

How can one even identify such a will-o'-the wisp? It is done by reconstruction. In each nuclear event, the tracks of five or ten or more longer-lived particles can be measured. Suppose that two of them (or maybe three) come from the breakup of one short-lived meson. We don't know which two. The method is to take each possible pair of tracks in turn and ask, "If these two objects came from the decay of a single meson, what would the mass of that meson have had to be?"

One then plots on a graph the distribution of masses so calculated. Most pairings will be incorrect; these result in a flat line describing the distribution of masses. The flat line is called the background. With luck, bumps will appear in the graph—a concentration of pairs (or triplets) all with nearly the same combined mass, forming a distinct peak standing above the background. Such a peak can be taken as evidence for the production of a short-lived meson.

Ting needed to use three different accelerators in his search for mesons. The energy of the beam has to be high enough to be able to produce the mesons. But if it is too high, there will be so much background that the meson peaks may be hard to distinguish. Each of the accelerators chosen by Ting is suitable for a different region of meson masses. The Brookhaven accelerator is best suited for mesons with masses equivalent to energies between 1500 and 5500 million electron volts (MeV). In the spring of 1974, the Ting group was at Brookhaven, tuning up their equipment for a search for mesons in this mass range.

An earlier group, searching for new mesons at Brookhaven, had been frustrated by their poor mass resolution. This group had reported not a bump but a "shoulder" resting indistinctly above a sloping background at a mass of about 3000 MeV. There may have been something there, but the data was not accurate enough to make firm claims. The Ting group was not about to fall into that trap.

The Ting apparatus was designed so that they could measure the mass of any pair of particles to a precision of 5 MeV. All the correct pairings of tracks from a decaying meson would fall into a single point of the mass-distribution plots. The background should be evenly distributed over many points.

This trick to suppress background works only if the graph of the meson's maximum mass does not cover a broad range—that is, if it looks like a sharp peak rather than a wide curve. Some mesons have peaks that are quite wide. The rho meson, one that the Ting group had studied at DESY, has a mass peak that spans the region from 700 to 850 MeV. Such large uncertainty in the mass-energy of a meson is believed to be associated with extremely short lifetimes. The longer the meson's life, the narrower its mass peak. Ting's experiments were designed to find relatively long-lived, narrow meson peaks.

The full beam of the accelerator was slammed into a

piece of beryllium metal. This was surrounded by massive amounts of shielding: all the concrete from an accelerator in Cambridge, Massachusetts, that had recently shut down; ten thousand pounds of borax soap to absorb neutrons. No particles could get out except through two carefully placed small holes in the shielding. Strong magnets placed at the exits to these holes deflected aside all except the fastest particles that emerged. Special detectors that responded only to electrons and positrons made sure that no other kinds of particles would be counted.

The Ting group first set the magnets to accept electron-positron pairs coming from possible mesons with mass between 4000 and 5000 MeV. The apparatus worked well; there was very little background. There were no mesons to be seen, either.

Late in August 1974, they reset the apparatus to cover the mass range from 2400 to 4000 MeV. Immediately they saw a strong peak. In the 5-MeV-wide region centered at 3100 MeV, the equipment counters registered decaying particles at more than ten times the rate of the background. No meson of any kind had ever been seen at a mass of 3100 MeV, more than three times the mass of a proton. Something exciting was happening.

Before they could investigate further, their beam time was up. Other experimenters were scheduled to use the beams at Brookhaven and were waiting for their turn. Ting wrote letters to the management pleading for more time. He hinted at the spectacular results his group was finding, but he had to be careful not to say too much. The results were not ready to be published yet. If word got out prematurely, it was still possible the some other experimental team somewhere in the world might scoop him on the discovery.

What could the new object be? Its mass was more than double that of any meson ever seen before. It decayed completely into an electron and a positron, at least part of the time. Its width was less than 5 MeV—possibly much less—which implied a moderately long lifetime (for a neutral meson) but certainly much less than the few billionths of a second it took to reach the hole in the shielding.

There was no lack of theoretical ideas. In fact, there were so many that it was hard to pick out the right one.

One of the more promising schemes was the quark model, which had been around more than ten years. According to this model, all subnuclear particles are combinations of a few elementary objects, called quarks. (The name comes from an obscure quote from James Joyce's *Finnegan's Wake*: "Three quarks for Muster Mark.") Protons and neutrons are supposed to be made up of three quarks. A meson is composed of one quark and one antiquark. Quarks themselves have never been spotted, despite intensive searches. It was not certain whether they really existed or were just convenient mathematical fictions that helped to classify mesons.

A neutral short-lived meson must be made of a quark and the same kind of antiquark. The short lifetime is just the time it takes for the two quarks to annihilate each other. The three kinds ("flavors") of quark originally proposed were known as u, d, and s quarks (for "up," "down," and "strange"). To each of these flavors corresponded one neutral short-lived vector meson: the already-known rho, omega, and phi mesons. Lately, however, it had been proposed to add a fourth flavor of quark to the model. In the tongue-in-cheek lexicon of particle physics, the new quark was to be called c, for "charmed." Perhaps the new meson that was showing up in Ting's data was a combination of a charmed quark and its antiquark.

There was no doubt in Ting's mind about what the new meson, whatever its composition, was to be called. No Greek letters were to be used for this particle. As its discoverers, he and his group had the privilege of proposing its name. Ting had in mind the capital letter J, ostensibly from the English alphabet. It was hardly a coincidence that this letter bears a close resemblance to the Chinese character pronounced "Ting."

By October 1974, Ting's group obtained some more running time. The peak was still there in the same place. They ran some checks to make sure that the effect was real. The magnet current was changed by 10%; the peak moved to exactly the position it should for a meson with a mass of 3100 MeV. Changing the intensity of the beam or the thickness of the beryllium target caused just the changes one could predict. So far as they could tell, the apparatus was not deceiving them.

Was it time to publish the results? Some members of the group were saying yes. Ting argued for caution. It would be embarrassing to rush into print and then find a mistake and have to confess the error in public. Also, there might be more mesons just waiting to be discovered. Why not find them all, while they still had the field to themselves, before alerting others to the search?

But even so, the information was beginning to leak out. Brookhaven management had to be kept informed in order to justify more running time. Melvin Schwartz, a Stanford professor leading the group that was competing for use of the beam, came into Ting's office and demanded to see the peak in the mass plot, which he had somehow heard about.

Ting put Schwartz off by betting him ten dollars that there was no such peak.

Min Chen, like Ting an American citizen who had been brought up in China, was making a strong case for publication. The scientific weekly journal, *Physical Review Letters*, which carried most of the important high-energy physics announcements in the United States, has its offices right on the Brookhaven site. On November 6, Chen and Ting visited the editor and verified that a brief, important result could be submitted and published within two weeks. Ting wrote a draft paper and gave it to the typists and draftspeople at MIT. It would take a day or two to prepare camera-ready copy.

Could anybody in the world possibly beat the Ting group to their discovery? Their proposals had already been accepted at three of the world's leading laboratories. Experiments that take years to design and build, and months to collect the data, cannot spring up overnight. But there was competition in an unexpected quarter.

A new kind of high-energy machine had recently come into operation, in the form of electron-positron colliding storage rings. In these devices, positrons—created in the collisions of fast electrons with a target of lead—are injected into an evacuated ring controlled by strong magnets. As long as the vacuum is good and the positrons are kept away from the walls, the beam can be kept for many hours. Electrons are then injected into the same ring, going around in the opposite direction.

Collisions between electrons and positrons in such a ring are rare. A beam of particles in a vacuum does not present one trillionth the number of nuclear targets as in a piece of metal. Perhaps once per minute, one electron will annihilate one positron. But there are compensating advantages in this kind of collision. The initial state, an electron and a positron annihilating to form a momentary situation of pure radiation energy, is simple and well defined. Moreover, all the energy of the collision is available to form new particles, since the collision is made of two moving targets, rather than the case of protons hitting a fixed target, as in Ting's experiment at Brookhaven.

By 1974 electron-positron colliders were operating in France, Italy, the USSR, and the United States, with one under construction at DESY. The highest energy collider was at the linear accelerator center in Stanford, California. The SPEAR facility there could collide beams at energies from about 1000 MeV up to 4500 MeV in each beam.

SPEAR was the creation of Professor Burton Richter. In 1970 Richter had persuaded the director of SLAC, Professor W. K. H. Panofsky, to begin construction of the storage ring using laboratory operating funds—money that might otherwise be used to pay power bills or the salaries of the operating crew.

When Ting and his collaborators were writing their proposals in 1972, they had considered and dismissed the idea of doing the search for new mesons at an electron-positron collider. Instead of having the meson break up into an electron-positron pair, one could try to form the meson in an electron-positron collision. The problem with doing this is that the electron and positron have to have exactly the right amount of energy. When protons bombard beryllium, different kinds of mesons can be produced with the same beam at one sufficiently high energy. At a collider, if the energy of the two beams differs from the meson's mass by more than the mass-width of the particle, the meson is not formed. If the energy is not right on the mark, the effects of the meson's presence cannot be seen.

A search for a narrow-width meson at an electron-positron collider can be tedious. One has to tune the beam carefully to each energy, take data long enough to record a significant number of events, and then change the beam to the next energy. If the scan has to cover a thousand steps in energy, and each one requires four hours of tuning and taking data, the search takes six months. Of course, if the experimenters know exactly where to look, the results can come in much sooner.

The first year of operation at SPEAR, 1973–74, was spent doing a survey. Data was taken at ten or twelve widely spaced points, between 2500 and 5000 MeV total energy. When running resumed at the end of 1974, they expected to continue the survey at still higher energies.

Looking for a narrow peak in this fashion is like looking for a single tree, which may not even be there, at night in a broad, flat meadow. One can grope around here and there. With luck one may brush against an outlying branch or trip over a root. A low but wide hill is easier to find; this is probably what the SPEAR group thought they were looking for. The best strategy is to look in as many different places as possible and come back for a closer search where it looks most promising.

Richter and his team expected that the rate of annihilation would probably vary smoothly with energy. Perhaps this rate would stay roughly the same at all energies; perhaps it would fall off gradually as the energy of the beams was increased. But the team was always on the lookout for structure, that is, bumps or wiggles in the curve of annihilation rate versus energy.

The first year of SPEAR's operation, 1973–74, produced a curve that looked fairly smooth, but with one or two points that seemed a little higher than the others nearby. These might be just fluctuations in the counting rate, but the data was suspicious enough that it was worth repeating them. At the end of June 1974, just before the summer shutdown, SPEAR was scheduled to repeat the data collection at a few selected energies, including 3100, 3200, and 3300 MeV.

The log books show that the experimenters were interested in possible peaks in the reaction rate. One entry reports with disappointment that rapid analysis of the data shows "no bump" at one of the energies. The experiment concluded on July 2, 1974, and the shutdown began. At the very moment that the Ting group was tuning up for taking data at Brookhaven, the physicists at SPEAR were carefully reanalyzing their data.

Dr. Roy Schwitters, a junior member of the SPEAR group, had the task of preparing the data for publication. He began the summer with the impression that the rate of reaction varies smoothly with energy. He had even written the first sentence of the paper saying just that. But then he found an error in the computer program. It was correcting for the effects of a cylinder of iron that had been placed around the beam at one time but was no longer there in June. The results Schwitters was getting did not look smooth.

The June data can be summarized as follows:

3300 MeV—"good." The data fits smoothly into a curve that passes through points at both higher energies and those below 3000 MeV.

3200 MeV—30% higher than the smooth curve predicts. No accident; the effect is seen in several sets of data taken at different times.

3100 MeV—Data is inconsistent. Runs 1384–1389 fit the

smooth curve. Run 1380 had three times the smooth curve rate. Run 1383 had 102 annihilation events, when only twenty would be predicted from the smooth curve.

Each of these "runs" lasted about an hour, until a reel of magnetic tape was filled, or else they had to stop to inject more electrons and positions into the beam.

What was different about runs 1380 and 1383? With hindsight we can speculate that they were not really at exactly 3100 MeV. The meson that lay waiting to be discovered is really at 3105 MeV and is very narrow. When the beam is properly tuned to 3100 MeV (as it probably was for runs 1384–1389) no meson can be produced. Runs 1380 and 1383 were probably a few MeV higher than the operators thought. On such small deviations do great discoveries sometimes depend.

In mid-October 1974, Schwitters showed the strange behavior of the reaction rate to his colleagues. Some of them began to examine run 1383 to see if there was anything else abnormal about it. Gerson Goldhaber soon reported that the events from this run contained an unusually large number of so-called K mesons. We know now that this was a mistake; Goldhaber was fooled partly by misidentification and partly by fluctuations. But even mistakes can be valuable if they trigger further investigation. The whole magnetic spectrometer group now became excited. They were sure they were on to something important.

The SPEAR operating crew, which had been preparing all summer for higher energies, was told to get ready to go back to 3100 MeV. The computer experts were making sure that the rapid analysis programs were working well. Somebody stored a bottle of champagne in the refrigerator, just in case there was something to celebrate. On Saturday, November 9, they were taking data.

They began at 3140 MeV and found a rate definitely higher than normal, similar to what had been found at 3200 MeV in June. To make sure that they really knew what "normal" was, they went down to 3000 MeV and got the usual low rate. Then it was back up to 3120 MeV, at which the rate was double the normal rate. Something significant was indeed going on there.

The night of November 9 was spent exploring various energies. The high counting rate did not show up anywhere else. The next morning, Sunday, Captain Richter took the helm in the beam control room. They were going to begin a scan, one MeV at a step, beginning at 3100 MeV.

At about noon they found a point where the rate was seven times normal. Nothing like this had been seen in particle physics before: a change in rate of a factor of seven with a one-MeV change in beam energy!

The physicists present, including Richter, Goldhaber, Schwitters, and Chinowsky, held a caucus. The effect they were seeing was so big, so unmistakable, and so unprecedented, that they would have to announce the results as fast as possible. Goldhaber volunteered to start writing a paper for publication. Richter showed him a quiet side office where he could begin this task.

Scientists do not normally write papers while the data is still coming in. The team at SPEAR recognized the importance of their discovery and the excitement it would create. They also understood the urgency of publication. The result would be easy to duplicate, since another storage ring in Frascati, Italy, could run the same experiment and witness the same peak. In fact, after the news reached Italy (by way of a member of Ting's group), the SPEAR results were duplicated there within three days.

Goldhaber had barely finished the draft—the report was

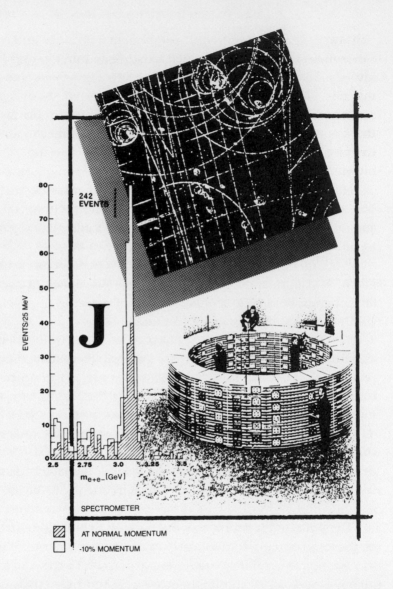

Sam Ting reported a peak in the mass spectrum of electron-positron pairs (*lower left*), which he named the J particle. Also shown here are tracks of high-energy particles in a bubble chamber (*upper right*), and a large magnet built at CERN laboratory, Geneva.

only two pages long, much of it taken up by graphs and by the names of the authors—when Chinowsky burst excitedly into the room. They had run at the next energy step, and the rate had gone up by another factor of ten, a total of seventy times normal! Events were coming in so rapidly that there was hardly time to keep count. Goldhaber now had to erase the numbers in the first draft and write in the new, higher values.

Now was telephone time. Calls went out to absent members of the collaboration, to laboratory management at SLAC and Berkeley, to theoretical physicists at both places, and to other colleagues. Some of these people must have called their own friends around the world. That was the moment when Martin Deutsch of MIT heard of the excitement at SLAC and telephoned Ting's motel in Palo Alto.

Professor James ("Bee-jay") Bjorken, then of SLAC, recalls a call from Richter during family dinner that day. Bjorken and Sheldon Glashow of Harvard had written an important paper predicting the existence of the charmed quark. After returning to the dinner table, Bjorken scooped a large helping of what he thought was sour cream onto his potato. When he bit into it, he realized to his intense discomfort that it was very sharp horseradish sauce. His wife recognized that the news he had just heard was indeed unsettling. "Bee-jay," she suggested, "I think you had better go to the lab now."

The counting house was filling up with people. Members of the experiment, accelerator people, administrators, visitors, all wanted to be present to participate in the excitement, to speculate about the nature of the new peak, to watch the data come in, to sip the champagne. The moment of exultation left an indelible memory on everyone who was there.

The shape of the peak continued to be traced out. Its highest point was one hundred times the normal rate, at 3105 MeV. It dropped off rapidly within one or two MeV to either side of that, a beautifully narrow peak. Even that narrow width was attributable to the fact that the beams themselves have a spread of energies. The natural width of the meson's mass-peak was later deduced indirectly to be only one-sixteenth of an MeV. A tail on the high-energy side reaches 3200 MeV. The rate here, 30% above normal, had been one of the early clues to the discovery.

By the evening of that Sunday, November 10, Burt Richter had written the final draft of the paper. A name had to be chosen for the new meson. At first the designation Sp-3105 was used, with Sp standing for SPEAR. Within a day, the Greek letter psi had been substituted, which had not been used for any previously named meson, and which contained the same consonantal sounds as Sp.

Monday morning the program advisory committee was scheduled to meet. Ting arrived at eight, spotted Burt Richter, and announced that he had some interesting physics results to tell. Richter rejoined that he also had some interesting physics to show. Considering the heavy telephone traffic of the day before, perhaps each of them had some inkling of what the other had to say. The revelations of that morning's session capped what must stand as the most amazing simultaneous discovery of an important effect in the history of physics.

The program committee soon adjourned in favor of a public seminar in the SLAC auditorium. The room was packed not only with physicists but with the nonscientific employees of the laboratories: secretaries, technicians, machinists, mail staff. Even if they did not understand the scientific details, they wanted to be present to witness this important event in the history of the laboratory. Roy Schwitters presented the results from SPEAR, and Ting announced his discovery. It was clear that both groups had brought to light different aspects of the same phenomenon.

Both groups submitted papers to *Physical Review Letters*, which were published in the December 2 issue, as was the confirming result from Frascati. By that date particle physicists everywhere in the world had heard the news.

Even before the publication date, new discoveries were coming out of SLAC. Hardly a day went by that some new fact about the newly discovered meson did not show up. On November 21, an extended energy scan revealed another peak near 3700 MeV. Its natural width is one-fifth of an MeV; the peak rate is only thirty times normal. The new meson was named the "psi-prime." Ting's group could not contest priority for discovery of the second meson. Their experiment was no longer taking data; the continued excitement centered at SLAC.

The existence of the second peak became public knowledge in record time. Richter persuaded the computer center to postpone a scheduled maintenance shutdown so that rapid analysis of the new peak could proceed. The computer center in its turn explained why in a message relayed to the teletypes of all the users, including those at other universities: "DUE TO NEW PARTICLE DISCOVERY . . . SYSTEM WAS NOT TAKEN DOWN THIS MORNING." Even if they had wanted to, the SPEAR group could not have kept the psi-prime secret.

Armloads of theoretical papers were produced trying to explain what the new particle is. Very soon it was understood that the charmed quark-antiquark model explains the properties of the psi, the psi-prime, and the spectrum of related mesons that were found in the following years. A quark and an antiquark form a simple system, the way a proton and an electron combine to form a hydrogen atom. The different mesons in the psi system (several more were found later) are like the different energy levels in the atom. With such a simple system to deal with, it is easy to make the calculations and compare them with results of experiments. Like the Rosetta stone of Egyptian archaeology, these mesons are the key to understanding everything else. The quark model has become the accepted way to describe the behavior of subnuclear particles.

Samuel Ting and Burton Richter shared the Nobel prize in physics in 1976. Both of them, of course, represented a large group of physicists, but the Nobel prize cannot be divided so many ways. They also continue to share the name of the meson at 3100 MeV. It is usually referred to as the J/Psi meson.

# 6. The Day the Dinosaurs Died: *The Asteroid/Comet Impact Hypothesis*

Setting:   1978–79
       *University of California, Berkeley*
       *Lawrence Berkeley Laboratory*
       *geological sites in Gubbio, Italy, and elsewhere*
Protagonists: *Luis W. Alvarez, 67,*
       *Professor of Physics, Emeritus*
       *Walter Alvarez, 38,*
       *Assistant Professor of Geology*
       *Frank Asaro, 51, and Helen V. Michel, 46,*
       *Nuclear Chemists, Senior Scientists, LBL*

*The greatest known catastrophe to life on earth happened 65 million years ago. Three-fourths of all species then alive became extinct. Creatures as large as dinosaurs or as tiny as one-celled plants and animals, whether dwelling in the deep sea or on land, were exterminated. Although some groups—including mammals, birds, crocodiles, and land plants—managed to survive, their numbers were also decimated by the dramatic events that ended the Cretaceous period.*

*How long did it take for all the Cretaceous extinctions to occur? We are still not sure. In an effort to answer this question, a group of scientists in California made a discovery of a different sort. They found that, at the time that the extinctions took place, the earth was struck by an extraterrestrial object as big as a mountain. Whether this im-*

TERTIARY | CRETACEOUS | JURASSIC | TRIASSIC | PERMIAN | CARBONIFEROUS | DEVONIAN | SILURIAN | ORDOVICIAN | CAMBRIAN

**MESOZOIC**        **PALEOZOIC**

The collision of a comet with the earth 65 million years ago, at the end of the Cretaceous Period, may have been the cause of the extinction of three-fourths of all living species including the dinosaurs.

*pact caused all the extinctions or was simply the last nail in the coffin, the release of energy equivalent to one hundred million hydrogen bombs must have had catastrophic effect on living creatures everywhere on earth.*

*The solving of the Cretaceous mystery can be credited to a group with an unusual blend of talents. Walter Alvarez knew about the clay layer that marks the boundary of the Cretaceous sediments. His father, Luis Alvarez, combined his wide knowledge and experience in physics with the curiosity to ask the right questions and the persistence to search until he had found the right answers. Frank Asaro and Helen Michel contributed their mastery of the techniques of nuclear chemistry to do the measurements that made the discovery possible.*

*As with other scientific breakthroughs, the story doesn't end there. The Cretaceous event was not the only giant impact that came at a time of many extinctions. There will surely be others to threaten our future, but probably not for many million years. Knowing the danger, and assuming we survive the crises sooner to come, future generations can prepare for, and hope to prevent, the next such catastrophe.*

"This," said Luis Alvarez, "is the most fascinating thing I have ever seen in my life."

Coming from a man who had been present at the first atomic bomb explosion, who had x-rayed the Great Pyramid of Egypt with cosmic rays and had been the first person to carry an electronic hand calculator in his pocket, this may seem like an exaggeration.

But Professor Alvarez was sincere. The object he was holding, and the facts he was hearing about it, were stimulating a rush of questions and curiosity of the sort that had marked the high points of his scientific life.

The fascinating object, the size of a cigarette package, had been given him by his son, Walter, who had flown out to Berkeley for a Christmas visit. It was a polished sample of limestone, sealed in plastic, from a site in Italy.

The rock had been formed, the young geologist was telling his father, at the exact time that the dinosaurs were going extinct.

The experimental physicist narrowed his eyes. Years of experience had taught him never to accept anybody's word on a scientific subject, not even his own son's, without the evidence to back it up.

*How do you know that?*

The limestone at the bottom of this sample, he was told, is made of shells that were deposited at the bottom of the ocean 65 million years ago. That was during the Cretaceous period, the end of the Mesozoic era, the Age of Reptiles. The layer at the top is from the Tertiary period, when there were no more dinosaurs. This sample is from the boundary between the two eras.

The conversation was becoming animated. Both of the tall, blond, fair-skinned men were on their feet. Their appearance and their accents are more redolent of Minnesota (where Luis lived as a teenager) than the Spanish-speaking lands their name implies. The family, which proudly preserves the names of its Iberian ancestors, has lived several generations in the United States.

An objection occurred to Luis, one that would later be used against them by others.

*Dinosaurs didn't live in the deep ocean. There are no dinosaur bones in your diggings. How can you be sure that they died out at the exact same time?*

Dinosaurs weren't the only creatures that disappeared after the Cretaceous. Three-fourths of all the species alive at that time became extinct. All the big animals died, but also a lot of little ones.

Walter Alvarez got out a magnifying glass. In the white limestone that marked the Cretaceous part of the sample, many little white circular shapes could be seen. They were the remains of foraminifera, one-celled animals whose tiny bodies are each covered by a calcite shell. The genus visible here, Walter said, is called *Globotruncana*. They are about one millimeter in size.

In the upper part of the rock sample, from the Tertiary period, the limestone is pink. And there is no sign of the foraminifera. The *Globotruncana*, so abundant in the rock less then one inch below, have disappeared as completely and as abruptly as if they had all died overnight.

*Aren't there any fossils in the Tertiary layer?*

Yes, there are, but you need a microscope to see them. There is a species called *Globigerina eugubina* that is found in Tertiary sediments, like this one. "Eugubina" is the Latin name for Gubbio, the town in the Umbrian Appenines where this sample comes from.

Luis was examining the rock sample intently. It resembled a roast beef sandwich made of two different colors of bread, viewed from the edge. The white layer at the bottom was the one with the visible microbe shells. The pink layer at the top had the microscopic fossils. Between them there was a stringy layer, about one centimeter thick, of obviously different composition. This boundary layer also came in two different colors. The lower half-centimeter was gray, and the upper half red.

*What is this boundary layer?*

It is made of clay. There is a layer of clay like this between the Cretaceous and the Tertiary at several places in Italy. Probably there are similar clay layers at other spots all over the world.

Until this moment, Luis Alvarez had never realized what a sharp and well-defined boundary there was between the two ages, nor had he appreciated how catastrophic the transition had been for almost every kind of life form. The clay layer was complete news to him. He wanted to know more about it, sensing that the clue to a great mystery lay within his grasp.

*What do you think caused the clay layer?*

Well, the normal limestone contains a small amount of clay. While the sea creatures were raining down their calcite shells onto the sea bottom, some mud was being swept down from the land by the rivers, and this got mixed with the calcite. After the extinction, Walter suggested, the calcite stopped coming down for a while, but the clay continued.

*How long did it take to deposit the boundary layer?*

At the average rate of sedimentation, it took about a thousand years to deposit a centimeter of limestone. But if the calcite stopped, and the clay kept coming at the usual rate, let us say five percent as fast as the calcite, the boundary layer might have taken twenty thousand years to deposit. That is still a very short time on a geological scale.

*Is there some way we could measure how long the boundary layer took to form?*

So it was happening again. Here in his very hands was an unexplained fact of nature, and Professor Alvarez was rising to the challenge. He was at an age when he would soon have to retire as professor at the University of California, but the stimulus of a new riddle could still set his brain cells firing as rapidly as ever.

He liked solving puzzles, and here was a riddle of major

proportions. How long did it take to carry out the Cretaceous extinctions? What caused them? The thin boundary layer of clay provided a clue, but not yet an answer.

Not that the question was a new one. The problem of the death of the dinosaurs is as old as the sciences of geology and paleontology. A large number of explanations had been offered ranging from Noah's flood to volcanic eruptions. Perhaps the mammals ate all the dinosaur eggs; but that would not explain what killed all the nonreptilian species. Perhaps there was a catastrophic climate change; but it would have had to affect all the continents and the deepest oceans as well. A conference of paleontologists in Ottawa, Canada, as recently as 1976, had debated all the possible causes of the great extinctions and reached no firm conclusions. As the tabloid weeklies would put it, "The scientists were baffled."

Luis Alvarez is one scientist who does not like to be baffled.

The boundary clay presented an opportunity to apply the techniques of physical science to the problem. Until then, most of the information about the Cretaceous and Tertiary periods was biological, namely, the catalog of species that could be found in each layer of rock. The paleontologists had not paid much attention to the boundary clay layer. For one thing, it contained no fossils. Even its existence was not widely known, in part because the paper that first reported it had been published in Italian rather than English. So a physicist had an open field to bring new insights into this intriguing problem.

One of Walter Alvarez's specialties in geology is paleomagnetism. The earth's magnetic field reverses itself at irregular intervals, once or twice in a million years. (The reason for these reversals is another puzzle, which we will not go into here.) The Cretaceous-Tertiary boundary falls in the middle of a half-million-year period when the earth's field was opposite to what it is now. Compass needles in that era would have pointed south. By measuring the orientation of magnetic minerals in the rock, geologists can tell which way the earth's field was pointing when the rock was formed.

The sequence of magnetic reversals can help to date the layers of rock. Since the magnetic field is worldwide, the magnetic sequence is the same for sediments formed on land or under the sea. So the disappearance of the dinosaurs, who mostly lived on land, can be timed to the same period as the boundary clay layer in the undersea sediments—give or take a few hundred thousand years.

The rocks that were formed at the bottom of the ocean were thrust upward during later mountain-building periods. At the Gubbio site in Italy there is an unbroken sequence of exposed limestone 400 meters high, which was laid down on the sea floor between 50 and 100 million years ago. It is an excellent place to get a complete record of the earth's magnetic reversals over a long and important period.

Walter Alvarez and his colleague, Bill Lowrie, traveled repeatedly to Central Italy to gather samples. There they had met Isabella Primoli Silva and learned of her discovery of the microscopic fossils (*G. eugubina*) whose presence marked the Cretaceous-Tertiary boundary so sharply. And Walter had conveyed this information and the rock sample, to his father, the Nobel prize-winning physicist.

Luis Alvarez's immediate thought was to apply radioactive dating to the boundary layer. His young colleague at Berkeley, Richard Muller, had just devised a new, sensitive technique and was looking for a suitable application.

The basic idea was to find a distinctive substance that could be expected to rain down on the ocean floor at a steady rate. The longer it took to deposit a given layer of sediment, the more of the substance would be present there. If Walter's hypothesis about the origin of the clay layer was right, there would be twenty times as much of the substance in a sample from the boundary clay as from the same amount of limestone above or below the boundary.

The test substance need be present in only tiny amounts. Muller's method was sensitive enough to detect as little as a few hundred atoms. The test material was to be some radioactive atom. These are produced naturally at a regular rate when atoms in the upper air get broken up by incoming cosmic rays. Then they find their way somehow to the bottom of the ocean. Use of Muller's method on Cretaceous sediments would require that at least some of the radioactive atoms survive for 65 million years.

The candidate atom that seemed best for this purpose was beryllium-ten. Its half-life was, they thought, 2.7 million years. Only one atom in twenty million would last 65 million years. It would be barely possible to detect the survivors. But then they learned that the radioactivity chart was mistaken; the half-life of beryllium-ten was only 2.0 million years. The survival rate went down to one atom in twenty *billion*, and there was no chance of the experiment working. No other radioactive isotope was suitable. Either its half-life was too short, or it could not be produced by cosmic-ray collisions. Muller's radioactive dating technique would not work after all.

The Alvarezes did not give up on trying to measure the duration of the boundary clay layer. Luis spent a lot of hours in the library reading old scientific papers, trying to understand the behavior of some rare chemicals. Most of his searches came up empty, but that is part of the game. You have to try a lot of wrong ideas, he knew from experience, before you are likely to come up with a good one.

One of his earlier research adventures had taken Luis to Antarctica. There he had learned that shooting star debris could be identified in the ice by looking for unusually high levels of platinumlike metals. Platinum is an expensive metal because it is so very rare on the earth's surface. But there is a surprisingly large amount to be found in meteorites, the rocks and pebbles from outer space that are constantly falling to earth in bright blazes of glory. The platinum-group metals—platinum, iridium, osmium, rhenium—are ten thousand times as abundant in meteorites as they are in the earth's crust. The explanation is that, in its early days, the earth was so hot that it was molten. Most of the iron, and the iron-loving metals like platinum, sank deep into the core of the earth, where they can no longer be reached. The meteoritic material, on the other hand, never went through a hot molten phase, so all the original platinum remains.

There is not enough of it that someone could earn a living grinding up meteorites and selling the platinum. But the case can be made that *all* the platinum metals that are now near the surface came there by way of meteor falls over the ages.

The right idea had finally come. The platinum metals could be used to time the thickness of the boundary clay layer. Being so rare on earth, they could not come from anything but meteors. Raining down on the earth, night after night, at a steady rate, they would burn up in the atmosphere or break up and fall into the ocean. The platinumlike elements, which are mostly insoluble in water, would settle with the sediments on the ocean floor. Not being radioactive, they would stay unchanged, exactly where they settled, until some geologist came to collect the samples.

So that was all there was to it. Measure the amount of platinum-group metals in the boundary clay layer. Compare it to what you found in the regular limestone. The longer the clay layer took to lay down, the more platinum metals it would contain.

Easier said than done. Any reasonable calculation showed that the amount of platinum in the sediments would be tiny, a few parts per billion. Conventional chemistry would never find it.

Certain techniques might be sensitive enough to detect such a small trace. In neutron activation analysis, for example, the whole sample is bombarded with neutrons in a nuclear reactor. Some of the nuclei in the sample can capture a neutron and turn into a radioactive isotope. The sample is then removed from the reactor and placed near a gamma-ray detector. The newly created radioisotopes emit gamma rays with precisely defined energies, different for each kind of atom. Precise measurement of each gamma ray tells you which kind of atom emitted it. Counting the number of such gamma rays tells you how many atoms of each kind are present. If it is done carefully, it may not even be necessary to separate the elements chemically. This is important, because one part per billion of a 100-gram sample is less than a microgram, hardly enough to see, let alone weigh accurately.

Luis quickly figured out that iridium is the best platinum-group metal for neutron irradiation. The non-radioactive isotope iridium-191 can capture a slow neutron, thus turning into iridium-192. This radioactive nucleus has a half-life of 74 days, convenient for laboratory analysis. It emits a gamma ray whose energy is 468,000 electron-volts, sufficiently different from that of any other element likely to be present, to permit identification.

The idea of using iridium to date sediments came independently to Luis Alvarez, but he was not the first one to think of it. Larry Barker and Edward Anders of Chicago had tried the method ten years previously on Pacific Ocean deep-sea clays. The Alvarezes had not read Barker and Anders' paper. If they had, they might have been discouraged right away, for there was even less iridium in the sediments than Luis calculated.

Fortunately, there was a first-rate neutron activation facility next door. In a building just across the road from Luis's office at the Lawrence Berkeley Laboratory, Frank Asaro and Helen Michel had a setup where they could routinely analyze thousands of samples per year.

Lately they had been doing studies in geochemistry and archaeology. They could take a piece of ancient pottery and measure the amounts it contained of twenty-five chemical elements, most present in only trace amounts. The pattern of trace elements is like a fingerprint, identifying where the clay for each pot comes from.

It is ironic to note that all the steps needed for the discovery we are describing had been taken more than ten years previously. The boundary clay layer had been noted at least as early as 1964. The iridium dating method had been tested in 1968. Neutron activation analysis, including the operation of Asaro and Michel in Berkeley, had been going on even longer. Here it was 1977, and the right combination of people, techniques, and experience was finally being brought together to solve the problem of dinosaur extinction.

Yet it was not a method that was so ready to be applied that several research groups were likely to come up with the ideas independently at almost the same time. If the Berkeley group had not put these techniques together, it might have taken another decade or more before the work was ever done.

Walter Alvarez, earlier based at Columbia University, had accepted a faculty position in the geology department at Berkeley. Now he and his father could consult more frequently about their mutual interests. That summer he was in Italy collecting samples, arriving in California in time for the start of fall courses. In October the two Alvarezes paid a visit to Frank Asaro.

Asaro listened politely to their presentation, but he was skeptical. He had seldom detected iridium in pottery clay; it was unlikely they could measure it in clay sediments. Recently he had tried to find iridium, in an unrelated experiment, in some rocks provided by Dr. Andrei Sarna-Wojcicki, and had not found any.

There were nonscientific considerations too. The Alvarez project had not yet received funding, so the work would have to be fit in around the geochemical measurements. A backlog of hundreds of such samples had been building up. Asaro also wanted to make sure that Dr. Sarna-Wojcicki felt no conflict of interest.

In the end Asaro offered a compromise. He would analyze twelve of Walter's samples, some from the boundary layer, some from various locations elsewhere in the limestone. If nothing came of that analysis, that would be the end of what he could do for them. The Alvarezes accepted gratefully.

Many months were to pass before there were any results. The gamma-ray detector broke and had to be replaced. The geochemists were clamoring for their own output, which had to take priority. It was April before the Gubbio samples were irradiated. Then there were several weeks of waiting, while the shorter-lived radioactivity induced in other elements of the sample died away. In June 1978, they were finally able to look for iridium in the boundary clay.

(*From left to right*) Helen Michel, Frank Asaro, Walter and Luis Alvarez examine a sample of rock from the Cretaceous-Tertiary boundary clay layer (*upper right*). Later, Asaro and Michel extracted the gamma ray spectrum (*upper left*) from the sample, showing the presence of iridium.

In the limestone away from the boundary, the iridium was barely detectable, a fraction of a part per billion. But in the samples from the boundary layer there was much more. In material taken from the red part of the clay, there was six hundred times as much iridium per unit mass as in the bulk limestone anywhere outside the boundary region.

This was completely unexpected. It could not mean that the clay layer took six hundred times as long to deposit as an equal thickness of limestone. The original rationale for taking the measurement was certainly wrong.

Where could so much iridium in such a short space of time have come from? There was nowhere on earth that could provide it.

The conclusion was unmistakable. At about the same time as the Cretaceous extinctions, something from outside the earth had deposited a large amount of material, including iridium, over a large portion of the earth, in a rather short time.

The details were debatable. What kind of extraterrestrial object had it been? How long did the deposition take? Did it happen exactly when the dinosaurs died?

But the fact that some worldwide cataclysm did take place is indisputable. That it coincided with the time of the death of so many species suggests that the process of cause and effect was involved. What remained was to work out the scenario.

It was time for Walter Alvarez to make his summer trip to Europe again. He intended to gather more samples in Gubbio, more carefully located in stratum than before, and from other sites in Italy. But if the catastrophe was worldwide, it was necessary to gather samples far from Italy and see if they, too, showed excess iridium.

Walter knew of a site in Denmark where sediments from

the Cretaceous-Tertiary boundary had been deposited under then-shallower water than at the Italian site. More importantly, he knew the geologists who had explored the site. There is a courtesy code among earth scientists that one does not go uninvited to collect samples at a site that "belongs" to someone else. A physicist like Luis Alvarez might snort at such restrictions; to him it was as if an astronomer who found a new galaxy could prevent everyone else from looking at it. But Walter understood the protocol of his own field, and he was not about to make enemies needlessly. He asked the geologists who "owned" the site to show it to him.

The Danish sample of boundary clay was to show an iridium concentration four times greater than that in Italy. By the following year the group had obtained a sample from New Zealand, by way of Canada, which also showed the iridium "spike." As samples have come in from all over the world, there is no question that the effects of the Cretaceous event were felt all over the earth.

Meanwhile data was gathered on twenty-seven other chemical elements in the rock samples (none of them platinum-group metals). Of those tested, no element besides iridium showed as much as a factor of two increase in the boundary layer. There were some differences, enough to show that the boundary clay had a different origin from the clay that was included in the normal limestone.

Wherever the boundary clay came from, the sediments snapped back to normal soon after the catastrophe. The samples from the limestone above and below the boundary matched each other, element by element, as closely as two pieces of pottery from the same clay bed.

What makes the iridium stand out in all these tests is that there is so very little of it in normal earth-crust material.

The research could have stopped there. The presence of the iridium excess in the boundary layer was important enough. Walter Alvarez did schedule a talk before the American Geophysical Union, which was given at the Spring 1979, meeting. So the results became openly known, if not yet widely acclaimed.

To convince the world, and themselves as well, they had to come up with some more answers. What was it that had hit the earth, and how had it caused the extinctions?

Maybe a star had erupted into a supernova near the earth. A supernova is a spectacular event, a giant star at the end of its life, which suddenly for a few weeks outshines the whole galaxy. Over the past thousand years, only three supernovae have been seen in our own galaxy, but many others more distant have been spotted by telescope. The historical supernovae made great shows, shining bright enough to be seen even in daylight, but they were safely thousands of light-years away.

If a supernova exploded close to us, the tremendous burst of radiation would certainly be catastrophic enough to destroy most living species. It would produce iridium, too. Supernova explosions supposedly produce great quantities of all the chemical elements and send them hurtling into space. It is believed that all the heavier materials that eventually form into planets and suns like our own originally were formed inside supernovae.

There were some obvious problems with the supernova hypothesis. To deposit enough iridium worldwide to agree with the new data, the supernova would have had to be within one-tenth of a light-year away. The odds are high against having one that close, but that doesn't prove it didn't happen. But it would be incredible for it to happen more than once in the earth's history. We would have to find a different explanation for the other great extinctions in the fossil record.

But there was a simple test they could make for this hypothesis. Supernovae produce all kinds of atoms, radioactive as well as stable ones. For example, they ought to produce plutonium.

There is no natural plutonium on earth, because all of its isotopes would have decayed long ago in the five billion years since the earth was formed. Plutonium-244 has a half-life of 80 million years (much longer than that of the fissionable plutonium-239 used in nuclear weapons). If some plutonium-244 were freshly made in a supernova 65 million years ago, most of it would still be around today.

Asaro and Michel set to work looking for plutonium-244 in the boundary clay. Late one Saturday afternoon, Frank weighed out the sample and was ready to treat it with hydro-fluoric acid to separate the plutonium. But he was out of hydro-fluoric acid, and the storeroom was locked up. He borrowed a flask of the reagent from a colleague who was also working overtime. "Take care," the colleague warned, "this bottle has been in the hood."

The "hood" is the carefully ventilated working area where radioactive materials are kept. Frank was anxious to prepare the sample for irradiation. Only much later was he to remember the warning.

The nucleus formed by neutron irradiation, plutonium-245, has only a ten-hour half-life. It has to be purified before the measurement, and it has to be done quickly. Frank and Helen spent the next night and day doing continuous chemical separations and Luis and Walter fed them pizza, chili, and encouragement.

The gamma-ray analysis showed a clear signal for plutonium in the boundary layer! As unlikely as it had seemed, the supernova hypothesis was confirmed. Great excitement reigned among the four scientists. There was no other way that plutonium could have gotten into the boundary clay.

Or was there?

Being careful scientists, Frank and Helen repeated the whole procedure on another sample of boundary clay. The plutonium signal was gone! They racked their brains for an explanation, and then Frank remembered the reagent bottle that had been kept under the hood.

What else had been in the hood at the same time, Frank inquired. Some nuclear chemists had used plutonium-244 for some other experiment, he was told. Twenty picograms, a speck too small to see or detect (before neutron irradiation) had somehow found its way onto the first irradiation sample.

The results of the first try were no good.

The contaminated sample was not wasted. The gamma-ray data from it was used in the article they eventually published, to illustrate that a plutonium-244 signal could have been detected if it had been present.

There was a different experiment they could try to test the supernova hypothesis. There are two stable isotopes of iridium, iridium-191 and irridium-193. They are always found in the same proportion, five atoms of Ir-193 to every three atoms of Ir-191. Presumably this was the mixture that was in the gas and dust out of which the solar system formed five billion years ago. Nothing has ever happened that would separate the two kinds of iridium or change the ratio between them.

But there is no reason why a new supernova should create the two iridium isotopes in exactly the same five-to-three proportions. So one way to test the supernova hypothesis is to see whether the iridium isotopes in the boundary clay layer are in the usual ratio or not.

This was a tougher experiment than they had been doing until now. Iridium-193, when it captures a neutron, forms a nucleus with a 19-hour half-life. It would have to be purified both before and after the neutron bombardment, to get rid of the background from all the other short-lived radioactivities. The group was set for a few more pizza-and-chili sessions.

There were also some troublesome systematic problems that had to be overcome. The results were very sensitive to where the sample was positioned, both in the reactor and in the gamma-ray detector. Luis Alvarez designed a suspension system using sapphire ball bearings to provide accurate location of the sample, so that reproducible results could be obtained.

The answer was that the boundary clay yielded the same ratio of iridium isotopes as any ordinary iridium bought from a chemical supply house or found in a meteorite. The supernova hypothesis could be put to rest.

Whatever had hit the earth in 65 million B.C. was made of material like that of our own solar system.

It was now summer of 1979. It had been a year since the iridium peak in the boundary clay had first been seen. Walter was once again in Europe gathering samples and giving short talks about what they had found. But they had not come up with a plausible explanation of what caused the extinctions.

Luis Alvarez now began a frontal assault on the problem. For most of that summer he was spending every waking moment concentrating on solving the problem. He came up with one idea after another, made the necessary calculations, and decided—in nearly every case—why it wouldn't work. Alvarez is his own severest critic.

Several of his ideas had to do with a large cloud of hydrogen descending on the earth. It would react with the oxygen in the air to form water, using up most of our oxygen supply. The animals would die by suffocation.

But no source of hyrogen would do the job right. An interstellar cloud of gas would take too long for the earth to pass through; the plant life could regenerate the oxygen before it got used up. The sun did not have the right iridium-to-hydrogen ratio. The sun could flare up as an ordinary nova, and this would explain everything, except the fact that only close double stars—which the sun is not—can become ordinary novas.

Early on, he had considered the idea that a giant meteor had hit the earth. But it was not clear how that could kill so many creatures. If it landed in the ocean, it would set up great tidal waves. But how would that affect dinosaurs in the middle of a continent halfway around the world? How would it even destroy one-celled sea-dwelling animals like the foraminifera?

He could calculate how big the rock would have to have been to deposit the iridium all around the world. A piece of meteoritic material ten kilometers in diameter was needed. There are a few such large chunks of matter orbiting around the solar system near the earth. They are known as comets and asteroids.

The difference between comets and asteroids is not great. Comets spend more of their time in the cold outer reaches of the solar system, so they are able to keep frozen a covering of water ice. Some of this boils off each time a comet comes near the sun, and this is the source of its long tail. Both kinds of objects can have rocky cores. For the sake of convenience, we will use the word *asteroid* to designate both comets and asteroids.

Alvarez considered models where the asteroid broke up in the earth's atmosphere. But a large object like this would not break up that way. Most asteroids would hit the ground with a large release of energy, enough to vaporize themselves and many times their weight of rock and mud. This would happen even if an asteroid landed in the ocean. A rock that size could strike the ocean bottom, even while its top was protruding above the surface.

What a spectacular blast that would have made! The energy released would have been equivalent to 100 million megatons of TNT. (A typical hydrogen bomb is "only" a megaton.) Earthquakes would rock every continent. A gigantic mushroom cloud, resembling a huge volcano explosion, would send enough dirt into the upper atmosphere to black out the sun everywhere for months.

Alvarez turned to an old volume in his library detailing the volcanic explosion at Krakatoa in 1883. Dust from that eruption spread quickly around the world, reddening the sunsets for the next two years. The Cretaceous event, if Alvarez's calculation was right, was 1600 times as big as Krakatoa.

Without sunlight, the plants would stop photosynthesizing. The animals that fed on them would die. The scenario for mass extinctions would be set.

Alvarez now proceeded to calculate the size of the impact object several different ways. The first was from the amount of iridium in the boundary layer, assuming it was the same worldwide and that it all came from the asteroid. A second way was from the thickness of the boundary layer itself. This was assumed to come mostly from the earth vaporized when the object hit. This calculation is independent of the first; it can be made even without knowing about the iridium. Both of these methods gave the same size for the asteroid, about ten kilometers in diameter, or the size of Mt. Everest.

It is also possible to estimate how often the earth might expect to be hit by an object the size of Mt. Everest. That small an asteroid is hard to spot by telescope and hard to guess its size when it is seen. But enough of them cross paths with the earth that it is plausible to speculate that once in a hundred million years, a big one should hit us. A better estimate comes from counting the number and size of craters on the moon and on the earth that come from large meteors (or asteroids or comets) that have already hit. Most of these craters were made by smaller objects, but the curve can be extrapolated. Again the estimate is that the earth would be struck by an object ten kilometers in diameter about once in a hundred million years.

Everything was fitting together. It was not proved that an asteroid hit the earth, raised a cloud that shut out the sunlight, and thus caused all the extinctions. But it was a reasonable explanation of all the known facts. Considering how hard it was to come up with even this scenario, and how many alternate possibilities Alvarez himself had considered and ruled out, it was going to be very difficult for anybody to come up with something better.

In a buoyant mood, Luis called up Walter, who was on his way to a paleontological meeting in Denmark. "How about if we all get on a plane to Copenhagen and announce our discovery to the convention?" he suggested. Walter was more prudent. He attended the convention alone and presented a cautious talk on the iridium findings, without the asteroid impact explanation. His interested audience consisted of Jan Smit, a Dutch geologist who had heard of the Berkeley group's results and found confirming evidence in some samples he had taken in Spain. The other paleontologists were interested in their own researches and weren't paying much attention to young Alvarez and Smit.

In the time since the discovery was announced, physicists and astronomers have usually been quick to accept the asteroid impact idea. Geologists were a little slower but have mostly been won over. The paleontologists have been the hardest to convince.

It is hard to dispute the evidence that a large extraterrestrial object hit the earth 65 million years ago. But it is possible to deny that it caused the extinctions. The extinctions did not all happen at once, some say, and definitely not at the same time as the iridium deposits. Those who side with the Alvarez team can counter that when the data is interpreted properly, all the discrepancies will disappear.

Some of the foot dragging can be attributed to the history of the earth sciences. Much of the rational nineteenth century was spent in a battle against "catastrophism." The argument was raised that all the earth formations can be explained as the result of gradual operation of natural processes, laying down sediments, raising mountains, wearing them down little by little over millions of years. Great upheavals are not needed to explain anything. The Alvarez hypothesis, bringing asteroids from outer space to explain the Cretaceous extinctions, counters the whole thrust of the earth sciences for the past century.

But the uniform application of natural processes can also require great catastrophes, once in a hundred million years.

It was time to prepare the results for publication. Walter was keenly aware that there would be fierce opposition. The paper would have to be carefully worded, every argument buttressed, and credit generously given to every source whose work had possibly helped their understanding. Of course, every scientific paper should be like that. But an idea as controversial as a theory for the extinction of the dinosaurs and coming from nonpaleontologists was sure to attract a siege of criticism.

The preprint, nearly ninety pages long, was ready in November 1979. A revision was issued one month later. Three years had passed since that vital Christmas visit when Walter Alvarez had first shown the rock samples to his father.

In January 1980, Luis Alvarez announced the results at the San Francisco meeting of the American Association for the Advancement of Science (AAAS), an organization that includes both biological and physical scientists. Hundreds of copies of the preprint were handed out to all comers.

The blue cover of the preprint stated that the article had been submitted to *Science*, the journal of the AAAS. The article itself, much reduced in length, eventually appeared in the issue of June 6, 1980. By then every interested scientist and newspaper reporter had long since read the preprint.

Subsequently, confirmatory evidence came pouring in. By 1985, unusually large concentrations of iridium had been found at the Cretaceous-Tertiary boundary at more than seventy sites all over the world. Most significant are places in New Mexico and Montana that were above ground 65 million years ago. The iridium deposits were not just an undersea phenomenon and therefore could not be explained by some brief change in ocean chemistry. The New Mexico find (by Carl Orth and his collaborators of Los Alamos) coincided with a sharp decrease in the count of pollen grains in the rock. The flowering plants had been hit as hard as the foraminifera.

Another iridium layer was found at a level between 34 and 38 million years old, another time of extinctions. This later iridium deposit lay at the same depth as a widespread layer of microtektites, glassy fragments that are associated with large meteorite hits. Now there is hardly any doubt that the iridium layers were caused by the impact of large extraterrestrial objects. Most scientists, including many paleontologists, also agree that these impacts caused some of the mass extinctions in the fossil record.

An important spin-off from the asteroid impact studies was the concept of nuclear winter. In trying to understand how the asteroid impact could have destroyed life all over the earth, as by shutting out the sunlight for a certain period, it became evident to atmospheric scientists that the explosion of a large number of nuclear bombs would also send large quantities of soot (from burning forests and cities) into the stratosphere. (The Cretaceous event released thousands of times as much energy as would the world's present total arsenal of nuclear weapons, but, of course, none of the radioactivity.) All that soot, if it does not completely shut out the sunlight, should at least lower the temperature all over the earth for a long period. The idea of a nuclear winter that subjects the survivors of a nuclear war to death by freezing and starvation—including those places where no bombs ever fell—arose directly out of the interest in the effects of large meteoritic impacts.

Another idea that has come out of this work is that occasional catastrophies are a component of evolution. The mammals could hardly have come to dominate the earth unless the dinosaurs had died. Natural selection favors the species that are best adapted to their environment. But once a well-adapted set of species becomes established, nothing short of universal disaster can displace them to make room for a different set. In this sense, catastrophe plays the same role in evolution that death does in individual development. There would be no opportunities for ambitious young newcomers if most of their elders lived on and held their positions forever. It may be that life as intelligent as ours can evolve only on a planet subject to recurring impacts with large asteroids or comets.

In 1984 the proposal was put forward that the mass extinctions do not come at random intervals, but regularly every 26 million years. No need to worry right away; we are halfway between two extinction eras today. Richard Muller and Walter Alvarez published an analysis of the measured ages of meteor craters that showed the same periodicity. Muller and others proposed that the sun has a dim companion (nicknamed "Nemesis") that orbits our sun with a 26-million-year period. When Nemesis comes near its closest approach—still far beyond the orbit of Pluto—it supposedly stirs up a cloud of comets that rains destruction on the inner solar system, including the earth, which can expect dozens of impacts over a million years or two. The extinctions need not all take place at once.

The search is on to find such a star. It is not easy, for the sky is full of dim stars, at unmeasured distances, and there is no inkling of which direction to look. If Nemesis is found, it will be a great triumph for what sounded to some scientists like an even wilder speculation than the asteroid/comet impact hypothesis. Whether or not the Nemesis idea holds up, the scenario that the impact of large extraterrestrial objects were associated with, and probably caused, some of the great mass extinctions of the earth's history would still be valid.

Nobel prizes are not awarded in the earth sciences. Luis Alvarez already had his, in particle physics. For the others on this project, their prize is the satisfaction of contributing to the solution of one of the oldest riddles of natural history.

The work continues. Asaro and Michel are working on a project that will enable them to examine, centimeter by centimeter, sediments from the earth's oldest to the youngest layers, for enhancements of iridium. Walter Alvarez is at work in his laboratory, too: the field where he collects geological specimens. Luis Alvarez is professor emeritus at Berkeley, but hardly retired.

One important question remains unanswered about the Cretaceous extinctions. How long did it take to happen? What is the time interval over which the boundary clay layer was laid down? The fact that these questions are still not solved points up the serendipitous nature of the discovery. It was in an effort to measure this time interval that the Alvarezes first asked Frank Asaro and Helen Michel to measure the iridium content in the clay layer.

# 7. The Little Green Men Who Weren't There: *The Discovery of Pulsars*

Setting:      1967
              *Mullard Radio Astronomy Laboratory*
              *Cavendish Laboratory*
              *Cambridge, England*
Protagonists: *Antony Hewish, 43, radio astronomer*
              *(Susan) Jocelyn Bell, 24, research student*

*In July 1967, Cambridge's new radio telescope began operation. It was designed to look for the "twinkling" or scintillations of radio starlight, a feature that helps separate pointlike sources from those that are more spread out. It was up to the young research student, Jocelyn Bell, to pore through miles of chart paper looking for interesting radio stars.*

*In August she began to notice twinkling from a weak source away from the sun, where the scintillations were usually low. She pointed this out to her sponsor, Dr. Antony Hewish. A seasoned radio astronomer, Hewish knew that such noise in the receiver might be caused by anything from a faulty automobile ignition to a launched space probe. But Bell persisted and found the same strange scintillations several more times, always at nearly the same location among the stars.*

*Soon the radio astronomers dropped everything else to begin a full-time investigation of Bell's radio star. They*

TIME (SECONDS)

TIME (SECONDS)

The Cavendish laboratory in Cambridge, where Jocelyn Bell analyzed the chart recordings (*top*) that seemed to be signals from little green men in outer space. They were actually emissions from a pulsar within the Crab Nebula (*center*).

*found that this source was emitting brief, regular pulses that varied wildly in size but repeated themselves with a precision that rivaled the timing accuracy of the best clocks. Further studies showed that the source was far outside our solar system but well within our galaxy. The size of the source could not be larger than that of a planet.*

*Could these be coded messages from an intelligent civilization? The scientists began to refer to this radio source as "LGM," for "Little Green Men."*

*However, when Bell looked further through the chart paper, she found three more pulsating radio sources with similar characteristics. Could the little green men be stationed all over the galaxy? Unlikely. The scientists began to search for explanations in terms of the physics they already knew.*

*The "pulsars" that Hewish, Bell, and their colleagues discovered, and that other observatories soon confirmed, were eventually explained as being "neutron stars," incredibly dense objects with a mass like that of our sun crammed into the size of one large mountain. Such exotic objects had been conjectured about before, but few ideas existed of how they might be formed or how astronomers might see them. The Cambridge discovery opened the door on a whole new field of astronomy—hundreds of pulsars were subsequently found—and made possible the physical understanding of the extreme state of matter inside a neutron star.*

There must have been times when Jocelyn Bell was sure she had been born ten years too soon. A decade after she began her research work, scientific data would be stored on magnetic tape. Computers would read, decode, and manipulate the data, reducing the output to a few lines of neat printout to be examined by human eyes. But then, if digital techniques had been in use at Cambridge in 1967, she might have missed out on her discovery.

Data processing in 1967 at the Mullard Radio Astronomy Laboratory was done by feeding the output of Antony Hewish's new radio telescope directly to the jiggling pen of four paper chart recorders. Each paper roll advanced one foot per hour, the four of them together producing ninety-six feet of squiggly red lines a day. The telescope had begun operation in July; by September there would be a mile of chart to analyze.

They had built the telescope themselves. Over a period of two years Bell, Hewish, and a handful of others had strung 120 miles of wire and cable between one thousand posts laid out in a field of four and one-half acres. The cost of the installation, including the hire of several students who cheerfully sledgehammered throughout one summer vacation, came to about fifteen thousand British pounds—thirty-six thousand U.S. dollars at then-current exchange rates—which was cheap even then.

As for all the chart paper, there was no other course than to sit down at the scanning table and unroll it, trying to keep up with the output. Tony Hewish was too busy to do this himself. The responsibility of operating the telescope and taking the first look at the data fell upon the lowest-ranking member of his team, a young research student working toward her Ph.D. degree, Jocelyn Bell.

Bell came every day to look through the output of the previous twenty-four hours; she could not afford to get much behind in her work. Radio telescopes can operate day and night. Sunlight does not bother them. The sun produces some radio waves, but not nearly enough to blind us to the radio light from the stars. For Hewish's purposes the most interesting data was expected to come in the daytime, from stars whose light was passing near the sun on its way to us.

Hewish had already observed that the empty space between the planets is not really empty. A thin cloud of electrons is out there, and its presence has an effect on the passage of radio waves. Deep space probes confirmed Hewish's findings by detecting the "solar wind" of charged particles streaming away from the sun. Hewish had found the interplanetary electrons from the way they make radio stars scintillate.

Visible stars twinkle because the air above us is not smoothly distributed. When different light rays from a star pass through different amounts of air, optical effects make the star appear to blink on and off, to scintillate. The effect works only when the light is coming from a nearly geometric point. This is the case for stars, but not for extended objects like planets. Planets do not twinkle. The visible size of a planet (even though it takes a telescope to see it) is large enough to cancel out the scintillations.

Hewish had shown that electrons in space can cause radio stars to twinkle in the same way that air does for visible stars. The largest concentrations of electrons lie within the orbits of Mercury and Venus. If we look at radio light passing through that region, we are most likely to observe the interplanetary scintillations (abbreviated IPS).

The IPS technique can be turned around to measure not the presence of electron clouds, but the size of radio stars. If a radio star is shown to scintillate, that proves that its angular size must be very nearly pointlike.

In the summer of 1966, Hewish and Bell had used IPS to study the Crab nebula. This very interesting astronomical object was about to become even more interesting. It is located in the constellation Taurus, between the horns of the bull, at the spot where Chinese astronomers recorded a supernova explosion in the year 1054. A star appeared suddenly at that position, glowed bright enough to be seen in the daytime, and then faded away. Through a telescope we can now see an expanding cloud of bright gas at the same place. From its present size and expansion rate, we calculate that the cloud has been expanding for nine hundred years.

The Crab nebula also contains a radio source having a complex structure. The larger part of it is about the same size as the expanding gas cloud. But there is also a small radio source concentrated at the center of the nebula. The fact that the small source scintillates shows that it is tiny indeed. Bell and Hewish were able to show that its angular size must be less than a few tenths of a second. In physical size, it could not be much larger than our solar system.

What Bell and Hewish could not tell in 1966 was that the small radio source in the Crab nebula is pulsating thirty times a second. The pen on the chart recorder had a response time of three-tenths of a second, not fast enough to follow such rapid fluctuations.

The hot topic in radio astronomy in the mid-1960s was quasi-stellar radio objects, "quasars" for short. "Quasi-stellar" means "starlike." For astronomers that means pointlike. A quasar has such small angular size that we cannot distinguish it from a star through its size alone. By contrast, a galaxy never appears pointlike, even at very large distances. The quasars are thought to be so far away that it is miraculous that we can detect them at all. If they are really as distant as they seem, they must be shining many times as brightly as any nearby whole galaxy. Even today, we are not sure what energy source powers the quasars. The story of their discovery, itself serendipitous, would take us too far from this chapter.

Hewish wanted to search for more quasars. He knew that the IPS method would help distinguish pointlike quasi-stellar objects from more extended radio sources.

To this end his team constructed the new four-acre telescope. Two thousand forty-eight dipole antennas were arranged in sixteen east-west rows. By careful phasing the array could be pointed north-south in any direction in the northern hemisphere of the sky. The beam width was one degree east-west, a bit larger north-south. The array could not be pointed east-west; the earth's rotation carried each star across the telescope's viewing window once a day. Any pointlike source would stay four minutes in the field of view as it moved across the one-degree beam width.

Three features of the telescope's operation made it different from all other radio telescopes and uniquely suited to the discovery that was made. For one thing, the whole sky was being scanned systematically every four days.

The wavelength and the time response of the instruments were also unusual. The antenna was tuned to a long wavelength of 3.7 meters, corresponding to a frequency of 81.5 Megahertz. In the United States this frequency lies in one of the television channels and is thus subject to considerable interference. However, Great Britain had fewer TV stations than the U.S., and this was fortunate. A relatively long wavelength was chosen because this was where the scintillation effects are strongest. It also turns out to be where pulsars are strongest, so this choice was also fortunate.

The response time of the circuitry (including the recording pen) was set at one-tenth of a second. Ordinarily, radio receivers are designed to average over several seconds, so that random noise averages out to zero. To observe scintillations, however, the system had to respond quickly to rapid changes in the signal level. This feature is also needed to observe short radio pulses.

Without these features—systematic scanning, long wavelength, and rapid time response—the discoveries in this chapter could not have been made. It is true that some of the largest telescopes could (and did) sometimes operate with rapid time response. Some radio astronomers, therefore, still kick themselves for failing to notice pulsars before 1967. The Cambridge telescope was designed in a way that just happened to be nearly perfect for recording the presence of pulsars.

The job of scanning the output charts was tedious but also exciting. The possibility of finding a new quasar was always there. Bell and Hewish found the sky was liberally sprinkled with radio sources that scintillate, candidates for being quasars. They followed the radio sources week by week to make sure that the scintillations became more pronounced, as expected, as the source position passed near the sun.

In early August, Bell recalls, "I became aware that on occasions there was a bit of 'scruff' on the records, which did not look exactly like a scintillating source, and yet did not look exactly like man-made interference either. Furthermore, I realized that this scruff had been seen before on the same part of the records—from the same patch of sky."* The source was passing overhead in the middle of the night, which seemed odd. At that hour the earth and the antenna are pointing away from the sun in a direction where there

---

*This and following quotations from Bell are from Burnell, S. J. Bell, *Annals of New York Academy of Science* 302 (1977): 685–89.

were supposed to be few electrons. How could there be twinkling at that time of night?

She pointed this out to Hewish, who wasn't ready to become excited yet. There are many sources of interference, he knew, that might cause a few blips on the chart recorder. It might be a refrigerator starting up or a noisy auto ignition. It might come from a foreign TV station or a satellite passing overhead. The scintillations lasted less than a minute, whereas a real radio source would remain in the telescope's field of view for at least four minutes.

Jocelyn Bell went back to the scanning table, reassured but not completely convinced. The following week, when the telescope scan reached the same spot in the sky, she looked for it again. And it was there!

It made the same irregular appearance on the chart, some spikes much larger than others, not filling the full four minutes. More important, it was coming from nearly the same position in the sky, not at the same earth time. After a week, it was rising half an hour earlier, like all the stars. Therefore, it could not be anything fixed on earth. It could not be an earth-circling satellite, either, for they cannot stay fixed with respect to the stars. Hewish checked with other astronomical observatories, the only people who use star-time rather than sun-time, to make sure they were not sending out signals at night when this particular star was overhead.

The stellar coordinates could be determined: declination 22 degrees; right ascension 19 hours, 19 minutes. In the northeast summer sky. In the center of the triangle formed by the bright stars Deneb (in Cygnus, the Swan), Vega (in Lyra, the Harp), and Altair (in Aquila, the Arrow). In the constellation Vulpecula, the Fox and Goose.

There are no bright stars in Vulpecula. (It is best known

as the location of the Dumbbell nebula.) There are no visible-light stars, not counting some faint ones in the vicinity, at the location of the scintillations Jocelyn had found.

The strange source kept reappearing. Not every time the scan passed its position, to be sure. Never for the full four minutes of the view field window. Randomly located within those four minutes when it did appear. After it had reappeared six more times, Hewish was forced to agree that it was time to look into this strange source more closely. He thought it might be some kind of flare star. They began to get ready to look at its behavior on a faster time scale.

The electronic techniques were improved to the point of following changes as short as fifty milliseconds. A Rapidgraph pen recorder was installed, a machine that could spew out a few feet of paper every minute. Of course, the fast chart recorder could not be left running all the time, since it would flood the lab with paper. Someone would have to go out to the telescope just when the radio source was appearing and switch on the fast recorder for the few minutes that it was in view. That somebody, naturally, had to be Jocelyn Bell.

She started going out to the observatory each day to make the fast recordings. They were useless. For weeks she recorded nothing but receiver noise. The source was gone.

As October passes into November, the constellation Vulpecula keeps more businesslike hours. No longer the midnight scintillator that it was in July, it now passes overhead in the late afternoon. This brings it into conflict with lecture hours, and so one day in late November, Bell skipped the observations to go to a lecture. The next day she looked at the normal-speed recording and saw that the "scruff" had been there.

The next time it passed overhead, she managed to catch it on the fast recording. She contacted Hewish, who was teaching an undergraduate laboratory in Cambridge and announced to him undramatically, "It's back."

Hewish's reaction when she described the signal was that it must be artificially produced. Bell expressed the opinion that it might possibly be coming from a star. She persuaded him to come out to the observatory at transit time the next day. Fortunately, considering the unpredictable nature of this source, the signal appeared again.

This day it was on the air loud and strong. At the appointed hour the pen on the chart recorder began to twitch. Almost immediately they recognized that the radio signal was behaving in a way that had never been seen in any astronomical object before.

The pen point would jump suddenly an inch to one side and return just as quickly to its normal position. It would stay quietly there for over a second, and then it would jump again. The excursions came as regularly as a pulse beat, forty-five times a minute, like a well-conditioned athlete.

Some pulses were bigger than others. Many were barely visible pimples on the chart recorder line. Sometimes it missed a beat entirely. But the spacing between them was exact, always one and one-third seconds. You could set your watch by the radio pulses.

A minute passed, and the pulsing radio source passed out of the field of view. Since the antenna array could not be steered east and west, they could not follow it across the sky. Tomorrow, when it came overhead again, would be the next opportunity to see it. Meanwhile, they could stare at the trace on the chart paper and speculate about what they were seeing.

It was not the scintillations caused by interplanetary electrons. These give smoothly varying, irregular traces, not sharp pulses evenly spaced.

Perhaps it was an artifical signal, coming from a deep-space probe launched by the Americans or the Russians. No, it had stayed in the same place among the stars for over three months. It must be far outside our solar system, or it would have changed position by now.

Hewish pulled out the old charts for reexamination. He had been puzzled by some small discrepancies in the apparent position of the source, from one appearance to the next. Now that he knew that the source was pulsating, he had a better technique for measuring its position. The new calculations showed that the object had not moved at all, with respect to the other stars, in all the time that Bell had been observing it. It must surely be located out among the stars.

The duration of the pulses provided a clue to its size. The pulses were shorter than one-tenth of a second. In that length of time a light beam, or a radio signal, can travel less than twenty thousand miles. The radio source therefore could not be any bigger than that, and perhaps much smaller. If the star were larger than twenty thousand miles in diameter, it would not be able to pulse, or turn itself off and on, in such a short period of time. Information cannot get from one side of the star to the other at a faster rate than the speed of light. Even if the star did manage to turn on all at once, we would not see it happen that way. We would see the nearest point turn on first, then gradually receive the light from the more distant parts of the star. A star as large as our sun would take over two seconds to flare up or to dim down. The source they were seeing could not be larger than one of our planets, they concluded.

The strange source also emitted extremely regular pulses, whose size varied in an unpredictable way. Were we receiving coded messages from an intelligent civilization on some distant planet? The possibility could not yet be ruled out. Tony Hewish soon began referring to the pulsating radio source in his notebook, as the "LGM." The initials stood for "Little Green Men."

For the next few weeks the mysterious beacon dominated the lives of Hewish, Bell, and the other members of the team who were drawn into the investigation. These included John D. H. Pilkington, Paul F. Scott, and Robin A. Collins. Throughout December and January the source remained strong enough to be observed nearly every day. Repeated observations left no doubt about the pulsating nature of the object.

Scott and Collins made use of another radio telescope owned by the laboratory. This two-acre array was less sensitive than Hewish's new four-acre telescope, but now they had the advantage of knowing exactly where to look. The LGM source soon showed up in the small instrument. This proved that the pulses were not produced by a peculiar effect of the four-acre telescope.

The two-acre telescope could be steered east and west. Using this feature, the radio astronomers were able to follow the source for as long as thirty minutes. The strange behavior of the pulses displayed itself graphically.

Most of the time the source is quiet, emitting small, barely detectable pulses. Irregularly, at intervals of about five minutes or more, it flares up. For a minute or so it remains active, making many large spikes on the graph paper, and then it is quiet again. Given this kind of pattern, we can understand why on any given day the odds are about even that the source is active during the four-minute viewing window of the four-acre telescope.

Pilkington set up a second receiver, tuned to the slightly lower frequency of 80.5 Megahertz, and connected it to the four-acre telescope output. The same pulsating pattern appeared as at the original 81.5 Megahertz, except that the lower frequency pulses were always coming a fraction of a second later. The whole exact pattern was displaced by one-fifth of a second.

Each pulsation of the radio source is thus really a trill, the high notes followed by the low notes. It can be compared to the "hee-haw" sound that a donkey makes. In a figurative sense, the strange object in the sky is braying at us.

There is a well-known explanation for this effect. Because of the electrons in space, the speed of radio waves is not quite what it would be in a total vacuum. The lower frequency waves travel just a little bit slower than the higher frequency ones. It is not a very big difference, but over a long journey the differences add up. The 80.5 Megahertz waves arrive here just a little bit later than the 81.5 Megahertz.

If this is the right explanation, we can estimate how far away the radio star is. We have to guess how many electrons there are between the stars, but Hewish's experience gave him a good inkling of that. The pulsating source in Vulpecula is about 400 light-years away. There are many stars that are closer to us than that, but it must be considered one of our neighbors within the galaxy, which is 100,000 light-years across.

As the Cambridge scientists followed the activity of the peculiar source over days and weeks, they began to realize the fantastic accuracy of the pulse rate. The clock that governed the pulsations did not lose one-tenth of a second in a day, a precision of one part of a million. We now know that the regularity of the pulses is such that it does not change over a full year by as much as one part in one hundred million. The time between ticks of this clock is 1.33730113 seconds.

There is a correction for the motion of the earth. We encounter the pulses one-quarter of a millisecond closer together when we are moving toward the source in our revolution about the sun, than when we moving away from it. This effect is well understood, and easy to subtract.

If the radio source is also a planet in orbit about its own sun, there should be a similar small variation in the pulse rate. Over the next few months Hewish watched carefully for such an effect. There was none. After being corrected for the earth's motion, the intrinsic pulse rate remained absolutely steady. He concluded that the source in Vulpecula is not in orbit about any other star.

What were the scientists to make of the strange pattern of pulses? The knew of no physical effect that could account for the minute-to-minute variations. Could it really be coded messages from an intelligent civilization?

Two big pulses in a row. Then four tiny ones. A single spike half the size of the first two. Four more missed beats. Two smaller spikes, a missed beat, and another small pulse. What kind of code was this?

Is this the sort of signal that "little green men" could be expected to send out? Did the message ever repeat itself? Were there mathematical cues, like prime numbers or perfect squares, to hint at a rational sender behind the signals? No such regularity could be discerned.

In the meantime, what was to be done? Should the government be notified? Perhaps other observatories should be alerted, so that the signals could be verified and followed over longer periods of the day. For the moment, however, the Cambridge group chose to keep the discovery to themselves. They did not want to be invaded by the media until at least they were sure about the planetary motion, or the lack of it, of the radio source.

Jocelyn Bell recalls feeling very cross at this juncture:

"Here was I trying to get a Ph.D. out of a new technique, and some silly lot of little green men had to choose my aerial and my frequency to communicate with us."

Meanwhile, the chart paper continued to roll. The LGM source was on the air only a few minutes each day. The rest of the time the four-acre telescope could still be devoted to its original task, routine scanning of the sky for possible quasars. But now the astronomers were likely to pay more attention to weak scintillations in the middle of the night.

Just before Christmas, Bell came to the lab after dinner one evening to do some chart analysis. Shortly before the lab closed, she spotted some "scruff" in an entirely different part of the sky, near Cassiopeia. She rapidly checked through previous recordings of that part of the sky and saw that it had been there before. The lab was closing, and she had to leave before it locked for the night. The newly discovered source was due to transit before dawn, and she knew she would have to be out at the telescope in time to observe it.

It was very cold, and something in our telescope-receiver system suffered drastic loss of gain in cold weather. Of course this was how it was! But by flicking switches, swearing at it, breathing on it I got it to work properly for 5 minutes—the right 5 minutes on the right beam setting. This scruff too then showed itself to be a series of pulses, this time 1.2 seconds apart. I left the recording on Tony's desk and went off, much happier, for Christmas. It was very unlikely that two lots of little green men would both choose the same, improbable frequency, and the same time, to try signaling to the same planet Earth.

She returned from vacation to find her desk piled high with unanalyzed charts. Hewish had kept the telescope supplied with paper and ink during her absence. She set to work diligently on the new recordings and quickly came across two more lots of scruff in addition to the one she had found before Christmas. All three new sources were soon confirmed.

Hewish now referred to the various sources as LGM1, LGM2, and so forth. But it was clear that a more serious name was needed. The early publications called them "Rapidly Pulsating Radio Sources." This phrase was soon shortened to "pulsars."

The designation of the first source in Vulpecula, the original LGM, became CP1919. This stands for "Cambridge Pulsar at right ascension 19 hours, 19 minutes." The source near Cassiopeia, with period of 1.2 second, is known as CP1133, and the next two are CP0834 and CP0950. A pulsar later discovered at Harvard University's observatory was christened as HP1506. In an earlier era of astronomy, they might have been called names like "Bell's star," or "Hewish's star." Modern usage is not so personal, but it does help tell us where to find each pulsar.

It was becoming clear that the little green men were not out there. How could they be at so many different places all over the sky? The steadiness of the pulsar rates was showing that these pulsars were not located on planets in orbit, even if they were smaller than planets in size. Some other hypothesis was needed.

Hewish thought the pulses might be white dwarf stars rapidly expanding and contracting. A white dwarf is a star that has run out of nuclear fuel. No longer able to burn brightly, it collapses under its own gravitation until it is only a few thousand miles in diameter, a dim cinder barely visible to the telescope. White dwarfs are small enough to be pulsars. But it is not clear that they can pulsate rapidly or steadily enough to explain all the data.

Other scientists at Cambridge were getting in on the

game. Sir Martin Ryle, the senior radio astronomer at the observatory, and his colleagues set out to establish the precise positions of the pulsars. They hoped to locate them closely enough to see if there is a visible-light star at the same place. However, none of the original Cambridge pulsars have been identified with a star we can see.

In February 1968, Hewish, Bell, Pilkington, Scott, and Collins published their discovery in the British scientific journal, *Nature*. They reported at length about CP1919, the source in Vulpecula. They mentioned that they had found three others but didn't reveal their locations. They offered the suggestion that the sources might be oscillating white dwarfs or "neutron stars."

A neutron star is an even more collapsed object than a white dwarf. It is a star with about the same mass as our sun, condensed into a giant atomic nucleus no more than a few miles in size. Such a bizarre state of matter had been predicted theoretically. Before 1968 no astronomer had produced any evidence that neutron stars really exist.

The pages of *Nature* were soon full of papers about pulsars. Radio astronomers all over the world reported finding new ones. A total of nine pulsars were known by the end of the summer in 1968. Hundreds of them have been found since then.

Astrophysicists were quick to offer alternate explanations. Among the favorites was some version of a lighthouse model. The pulsar is not oscillating in and out, as Hewish had suggested, but rotating rapidly on its axis. Somehow it is emitting a beam of radio waves in one direction. As that direction sweeps past the earth, we receive a brief pulse of radio light. The variations in signal size from pulse to pulse, and from minute to minute, and month to month, have to do with the flickering nature of the searchlight beam. The accurate repetition rate reflects the steady rotation of the star itself.

Thomas Gold of Cornell University made the suggestion that is now accepted. The pulsars cannot be rotating white dwarfs, because a star that large, rotating as rapidly as the fastest pulsars are known to pulsate, would tear itself apart. It must be much smaller than a white dwarf, perhaps as small as a neutron star.

The neutron star might have a magnetic field, as many stars do. That field might be off-axis, as the earth's field is. Electrons spiraling along the magnetic field lines create radiation of all kinds, somewhat in the manner of auroras above the earth's magnetic poles. The radio storm associated with these spiraling electrons forms the radio beacon that sweeps over the sky once each rotation period.

The observation that confirmed Gold's model was the discovery at the end of 1968 that the small radio source in the Crab nebula is a pulsar. This is the same source that Hewish and Bell had studied a year before they came upon CP1919.

What makes the Crab nebula pulsar different from the ones discovered earlier is that (1) it pulses thirty times a second (which finally ruled out white dwarfs); (2) it is observably slowing down; (3) it can be identified with a faint visible star, which also pulsates at the same rate; (4) we know that it had its origin in a supernova explosion.

The standard explanation of pulsars is then complete. When a giant star undergoes a supernova explosion, the material in its inner core often is compressed into a neutron star. The neutron star begins life spinning rapidly, having a very strong magnetic field not aligned with the rotation axis. As the pulsar emits radio energy, its rotation rate slows down. Most of the pulsars that we observe were formed in prehistoric times and have lost nearly all of their kinetic energy. They still continue to rotate once per second or so, and they emit by the lighthouse mechanism the weak radio pulses of the sort that were first observed by Jocelyn Bell on that summer night in 1967.

Antony Hewish and Martin Ryle shared the 1974 Nobel prize, honoring the discovery of pulsars among their other accomplishments in radio astronomy.

The discovery of pulsars at Cambridge, when the radio astronomers were really looking for the twinkling of quasars, has opened the door to the study of a new state of matter. Who could have imagined the mass of a star as big as our sun, collapsed into a giant atomic nucleus the size of a mountain? As one of these scientists' compatriots* once put it,

There are more things in heaven and earth, Horatio,
Than are dreamt of in your philosophy.

---

*Shakespeare, *Hamlet,* act 1, sc. 5.

# Selected Bibliography by Subject

## Serendipity

Cannon, W. B. "The Role of Chance in Discovery." *Scientific Monthly* 50 (1940): 204–209.

## X Rays

Glasser, Otto. *Dr. W. C. Roentgen.* 2d ed. Springfield, Ill.: Charles C. Thomas, 1958.

Krafft, Ernest. "W. C. Roentgen: His Friendship With Ludwig Zehnder." *New York State Journal of Medicine.* 73 (1973): 1002–8.

Nicolle, Jacques. *Wilhelm Conrad Roentgen et l'ere des rayons X.* Paris: Editions Seghers, 1965.

Nitske, W. Robert. *The Life of Wilhelm Conrad Roentgen, Discoverer of the X Ray.* Tucson, Ariz.: University of Arizona Press, 1971.

## Electromagnetism

*Danish Journal* (August 1977). Special edition commemorating the 200th anniversary of the Danish scientist H. C. Oersted's birth.

Dibner, Bern. *Oersted and the Discovery of Electromagnetism.* 2d ed. Norwalk, Conn.: Burndy Library, 1962.

Meyer, Kirstine, ed. *The Scientific Life and Works of H. C. Oersted.* Copenhagen: A. F. Hoest & Son, 1920.

Nielsen, J. Rud. "Hans Christian Oersted—Scientist, Humanist, and Teacher." *American Physics Teacher* 7 (1939): 10–22.

## Penicillin

Bullock, W. A. C. *The Man Who Discovered Penicillin.* London: Faber & Faber, 1963.

Hare, Ronald. *The Birth of Penicillin.* London: George Allen & Unwin, 1970.

Ludovici, L. J. *Fleming, Discoverer of Penicillin.* Bloomington: Indiana University Press, 1955.

MacFarlane, Gwyn. *Alexander Fleming, The Man and the Myth.* Cambridge, Mass.: Harvard University Press, 1984.

Maurois, Andre. *The Life of Sir Alexander Fleming.* New York: E. P. Dutton, 1959.

## Cosmic Microwave Background Radiation

Bernstein, Jeremy. *Three Degrees Above Zero.* New York: Charles Scribner's Sons, 1984.

Gregor, Arthur. *Bell Laboratories: Inside the World's Largest Communications Center.* New York: Charles Scribner's Sons, 1972.

Penzias, A. A. and Wilson, R. W. "A Measurement of Excess Antenna Temperature at 4080 Mc/s." *Astrophysical Journal 142* (1965): 419–21.

Penzias, Arno A. "The Origin of the Elements." *Reviews of Modern Physics* 51 (1979): 425–31.

Weinberg, Steven. *The First Three Minutes.* New York: Basic Books, 1977.

Wilson, R. W. "The Cosmic Microwave Background Radiation." *Reviews of Modern Physics* 51 (1979): 433–45.

## J/Psi Meson

Abrams, G. S., et al. "Discovery of a Second Narrow Resonance in $e + e -$ Annihilation." *Physical Review Letters* 33 (1974): 1453.

Aubert, J. J., et al. "Experimental Observation of a Heavy Particle J." *Physical Review Letters* 33 (1974): 1404.

Augustin, J. E., et al. "Discovery of a Narrow Resonance in $e + e -$ Annihilation." *Physical Review Letters* 33 (1974): 1406.

Bjorken, James D. "The November Revolution—A Theorist Reminisces." *SLAC Beam Line,* no. 8 (July 1985): 1–6.

Goldhaber, G. "The Discovery of Charm." In *50 Years of Weak Interactions: Wingspread Conference,* edited by David Cline and Gail Riedasch, 392–408. Madison, Wis.: University of Wisconsin, 1984.

Maglich, Bogdan, ed. *Adventures in Experimental Physics* Volume 5, Chapter 4, pp. 113–65. Princeton, N.J.: World Science Education, 1976.

## Asteroid/Comet Impact Hypothesis

Alvarez, L. W.; W. Alvarez,; F. Asaro,; and H. V. Michel. "Extraterrestrial Cause for the Cretaceous-Tertiary Extinction: Experimental Results and Theoretical Explanation." *Science* 207 (1980): 1095–1108.

Alvarez, Luis W. *Autobiography.* (Forthcoming) San Francisco: Harper & Row.

Asaro, Frank. "Chronological History of the K-T Iridium Anomaly and the Asteroid Impact Theory." In *Selected Works of Luis Alvarez With Commentary*, edited by W. P. Trower. Forthcoming, 1986.

Muller, Richard A. "An Adventure in Science." *New York Times Magazine*, March 24, 1985.

## Pulsars

Bell, S. J. and Hewish, A. "Angular Size and Flux Density of the Small Source in the Crab Nebula at 81.5 Mc/s." *Nature* 213 (March 25, 1967): 1214–16.

Burnell, S. J. Bell. *Annals of the New York Academy of Sciences* 302 (1977): 685–89.

Hewish, A. W. "Pulsars." *Scientific American* 219, no. 4 (October 1968): 25–35.

Hewish, A. W.; Bell, S. J.; Pilkington, J. D. H.; Scott, P. F.; and Collins, R. A. "Observation of a Rapidly Pulsating Radio Source." *Nature* 217 (February 24, 1968): 709–13.

Kellermann, K. and Shuto, B. eds. *Serendipitous Discoveries in Radio Astronomy*. Green Bank, W. Va.: National Radio Astronomy Observatory, 1983.

Smith, F. G. and Hewish, A. *Pulsating Stars*. London: MacMillan, 1968.

# Index